It's another Quality Book from CGP

This book is for 7-8 year olds.

Whatever subject you're doing it's the same
old story — there are lots of facts and you've just got
to learn them. KS2 English is no different.

Happily this CGP book gives you all that important
information as clearly and concisely as possible.

It's also got some daft bits in to try and make the whole
experience at least vaguely entertaining for you.

What CGP is all about

Our sole aim here at CGP is to produce the highest quality
books — carefully written, immaculately presented and
dangerously close to being funny.

Then we work our socks off to get them out to you
— at the cheapest possible prices.

Contents

Published by Coordination Group Publications Ltd.

Contributors:
Simon Cook
Taissa Csáky
Gemma Hallam
Simon Little
Iain Nash
Andy Park
Glenn Rogers

ISBN-10: 1 84146 159 8
ISBN-13: 978 1 84146 159 5

Groovy website: www.cgpbooks.co.uk
Jolly bits of clipart from CorelDRAW®
Printed by Elanders Hindson Ltd, Newcastle upon Tyne.

Phonemes

Phonemes are all the different **sounds** that make up words.
There's usually more than one spelling for each phoneme.

Th<u>ey</u> m<u>ay</u> catch the tr<u>ai</u>n.

These are all the **same phoneme**, but they're not spelt the same.

Q1   Circle the phoneme with the same sound as the red letters.

Most people mow their own grass.   (ee, (oh))

He wanted to play.   (i, o)

The girl looked through the window.   (oo, ee)

The boy rode around the corner.   (aw, ow)

Q2   Draw lines to match up words with the same phonemes.

grain	coat
her	treat
claw	foot
blue	fort
coil	bird
though	moon
push	tray
meet	boy

Phone home?

No... Phoneme!

2

Syllables

Syllables are the sound units in words, a bit like the beats in a piece of music.

Syl-la-ble
1   2   3

This is a 3-syllable word.

dog   cat

These are 1-syllable words.

zeb-ra

This is a 2-syllable word.

Q1 Divide these two-syllable words into their different parts.

he|llo   goodbye   coffee

donkey   bathroom   hopeless

beetroot   breakfast   smelly

flipper   summer   lightning

Q2 Write on the dotted lines how many syllables there are in these words.

inspector — 3

doubtful — ....

spotlight — ....

wonderful — ....

strong — ....

suddenly — ....

English — ....

when — ....

fearless — ....

poisonous — ....

Syllables

Q3 Write out the separate syllables in these words.

neighbourhood — ....neigh.... + ...bour.... + ...hood....

essential — .... + ... + ...

pizza — .... + ...

row — ....

pastry — .... + ...

marvellous — .... + ... + ...

passenger — .... + ... + ...

Q4 Join the columns to make two-syllable words, then write out the words.

ba	age	....
sur	cial	....
thor	der	....
let	ough	....
saus	by	....baby....
lad	ter	....
spe	prise	....

Verbs

Verbs are the **doing** or **being** words in a sentence.
The **coloured** words below are verbs. Every sentence must have at least one.

She *is falling*.

He *runs*.

They *are* cold.

Q1 Circle the verbs in these sentences.

She (swims.)   Jenny jumps.

Kenny cut himself.   Billy is bouncing.

Charlie is chirping.   Rhonda was riding.

David plays tennis.   Ian was ill.

Q2 Pick out the verbs from this jumbled lot.
Write them in the spaces to the right.

went   see   ....

  daffodil   ......went......

carefully   pray   ....

    remind   ....

strange   fridge

Eeeeeeee!!

Q3 Circle the verbs in these sentences.

The boy (ate) the cake.

                                The mouse squeaked loudly.

Batman called to Robin.

                                Bananaman flew to the rescue.

Verbs

Q4 Draw a line from each verb to the picture that goes with it.

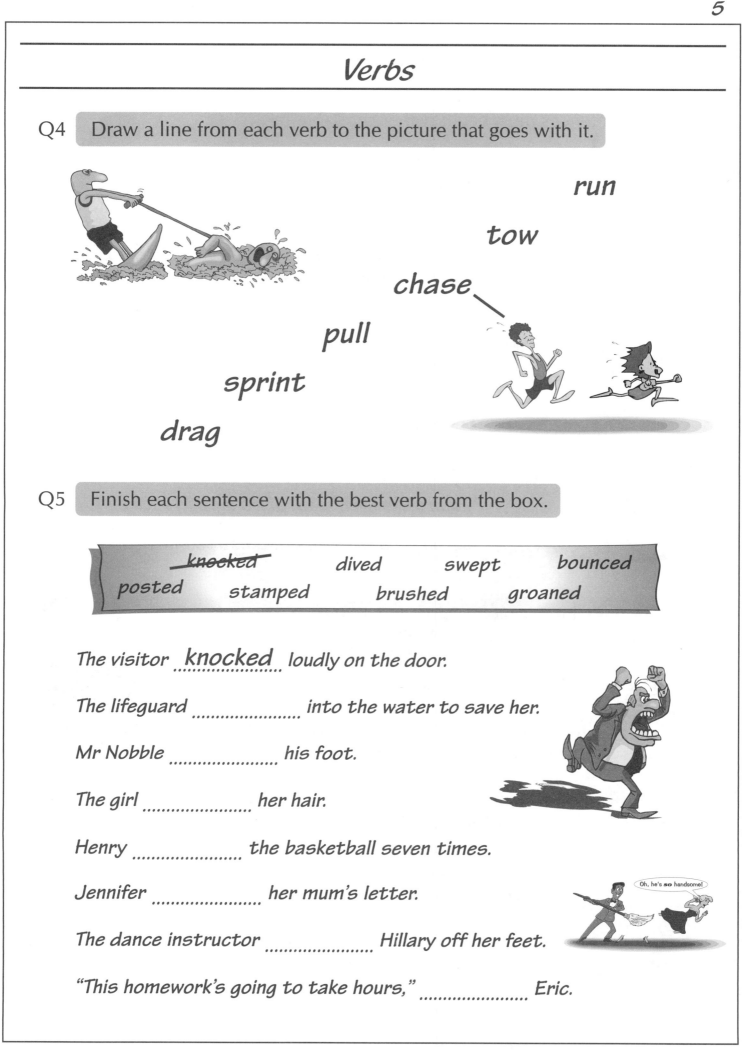

run

tow

chase

pull

sprint

drag

Q5 Finish each sentence with the best verb from the box.

~~knocked~~   dived   swept   bounced

posted   stamped   brushed   groaned

The visitor __knocked__ loudly on the door.

The lifeguard .... into the water to save her.

Mr Nobble .... his foot.

The girl .... her hair.

Henry .... the basketball seven times.

Jennifer .... her mum's letter.

The dance instructor .... Hillary off her feet.

"This homework's going to take hours," .... Eric.

Oh, he's *so* handsome!

Capital Letters and Full Stops

All sentences must begin with a **capital letter**...

My aunt's tea caught fire.

...and end with a **full stop**,
unless there's some other punctuation mark.

Q1 The sentences below don't have any full stops.
Put the full stops in the right places.

Mark liked the wind in his hair

Sandra liked roast cucumber sandwiches

"I don't like lard," said Jim I agreed with him

It's only eight o'clock It's not too late

Q2 Rewrite these sentences, putting in the
missing capital letters and full stops.

little Lenny just loved eating trees

....

the old man had green hair

....

baby Frieda loved licking lollipops

....

my neighbour trod on her marshmallows

....

she bought some shoes made from kippers

....

Questions and Exclamations

Some sentences are **exclamations**, and some are **questions**.
They both have their own different endings.

A question always ends with a **question mark**.

What's that?

Wow!

An exclamation ends in an **exclamation mark**.

Exclamation

Question

Q1 Write down whether each sentence is a **question** or an **exclamation**.

Where are you going? .....question.....

Look out! ....

What's happening here then? ....

How are you? ....

We've scored! ....

Q2 Add the right punctuation mark to the end of these.

Who's there.....   Ouch.....

It's a motorbike.....   What a surprise.....

Which one do you want.....   What is that.....

Go away.....   How do you do that then.....

What's the time.....   No way.....

Spelling '-ing' Words

There are a few rules that you have to follow when you add -ing to a verb.

When these people pull, they are 'pulling'.

Some words don't change — you just put the -ing on the end.

Q1 Add -ing to these words.

pass	.....*passing*.........	go	....
do	....	think	....
sleep	....	fight	....
feel	....	rust	....

Sometimes you need to double the last letter before the -ing.

Q2 Add the extra letter to these words, then complete the -ing word.

hit	.....*hitting*.........	stop	....
swim	....	skip	....
rub	....	flap	....
rap	....	spit	....

Q3 Add -ing to the words in these sentences.

a) I went swim**ming**......... yesterday.

b) Ben is dig............... his way to Australia.

c) Amy was tip.................. sand over the floor.

d) Denise went shop............... in town.

e) Marco was flap............... his arms like mad.

Spelling '-ing' Words

When a word ends in **-e**, you have to get rid of it before adding the **-ing**.

Q4 Try this here — drop the **-e**, and add the **-ing**.

make .... *making* ....

ride ....

shake ....

Kevin is .... in the armchair.   (hide)

Jane is .... the dog for a walk. (take)

Here's the difficult one though. If there's an **i** before the **-e**, then you must change the **i** to a **y** before you add the **-ing**.

Q5 Add **-ing** to these words.

Do your ears hang low?
Can you swing them to and fro?
Can you tie them like a ribbon?
Can you tie them in a bow?

tie .... *tying* ....

die ....

lie ....

Q6 Add **-ing** to the verbs below to fill the gaps in the sentences.

bake   slip   fall   dance   carry

The chefs have been .... *baking* .... cakes.

Marco is .... a huge cake.

Tony is .... on a banana skin.

He looks like he's ....

In fact, he's ....

Speech Marks

Speech marks show you when someone's speaking.
They go around the words that are spoken.

Gerald said, "I've caught it."

There's always some sort of punctuation mark **inside**
the speech marks, at the end of what the person's said.

Q1 Put speech marks in these sentences.

a) "I've got a lovely bunch of coconuts," said Anna.

b) You can't play football on the dinner table, said Pete .

c) There's a hole in that bucket, said Dave.

d) Oh dear, this doesn't look right, said Kirsty.

e) I see no ships, said Captain Pugnose.

f) I don't know where they are, replied Aisha.

g) Can you mend my bike? asked Luke.

h) Tom said, You can't fit a pig in a paper bag!

Q2 Fill in the gaps in these sentences. Use 'said', 'asked' or 'replied'.

a) "Can you peel those potatoes?" ......*asked*...... Martha.

b) "Only if you give me a potato peeler," .... Mary.

c) Martha .... , "There's someone at the door."

d) "Who is it?" .... Mary.

e) "It's a small blue monster," .... Martha

f) "Would you like to buy some towels?" .... the small blue monster.

Speech Marks

Whenever someone **starts to speak**, the first word always has a capital letter.

↓

I said, "There's a capital letter."

Q3 Write these sentences out with the speech marks and capital letters in the right places.

a) You haven't tidied your room, shouted Dad.

 "You haven't tidied your room," shouted Dad.

b) Bernice said, it's no good, I'll never know my times tables.

....

c) Graham said, this elephant smells a bit funny.

....

d) Sally whispered, the moon reminds me of marshmallows.

....

Q4 Use the words in the cloud to fill in the gaps in these sentences.

replied   squealed   muttered
~~asked~~   shouted   yelled

"What's in that box, Jim?" asked Barney.

"Nothing, Barney, it's just a box," .... Jim.

"I don't believe you," .... Barney.

"Don't!" .... Jim.

"Ow! It bit me!" .... Barney.

"Mum! Barney's trying to kill my hamster!" .... Jim.

Bip-a-bee-do-do-de-do-do
Bip-a-bee-do-do-do-do...

Commas in Lists

Whenever you write a list of things, you need commas.

milk, mayonnaise, magazines and monsters

You need commas between all the things in the list, except the last two. They just need '**and**' or '**or**'.

Q1 Put a circle around the commas in these sentences.

a) Don't forget to buy chocolate, cheese and a baked bean.

b) Make sure you've got a spoon, a knife, a fork and a spongecake.

c) I can see a man, a dog, a cow and a spaceship.

d) You can have tea, coffee, cocoa or a cold drink.

Q2 Put commas into these lists.

a) I dropped my notes a pen a pencil and a donkey.

b) We saw lions elephants giraffes zebras and gibbons.

c) Do you want lemming squash beetroot juice or camel soup?

d) They gave us a choice of catfish dogfish swordfish or goldfish.

Q3 Write these lists out with commas instead of all those '**and**'s and '**or**'s.

a) There are sandwiches and crisps and cakes and biscuits.

....

b) We could play tennis or badminton or football or netball.

....

c) I want a computer game and some Lego and a fluffy toy and a bike.

....

Commas in Lists

Sometimes you use several words to write about each thing in a list.

A packet of crisps, some cheese sandwiches, a raspberry yoghurt and a mouldy potato.

You still need to put a comma between each thing in the list.

Q4 Put commas into these lists.

a) I've just eaten a plate of beans a squashed cabbage three bulbs of garlic and a load of fairy cakes.

b) Martians have long spiky fingers big eyes very curly ears wrinkled green skin really tall antennae and pointy teeth.

Q5 Use the words below to finish off the sentences. Each list should have at least four things in it.

a fast car   a shirt   a teddy bear   a pair of scissors

a broken skateboard   a pair of sunglasses   a pair of football boots

a tube of toothpaste   a pencil   a holiday to Mars   a plant

a) Xena went to the shops and bought ....

....

b) In this room I can see ....

....

c) For Christmas, my mum wants ....

....

Prefixes

Prefixes are groups of letters at the **start** of some words.

wrap 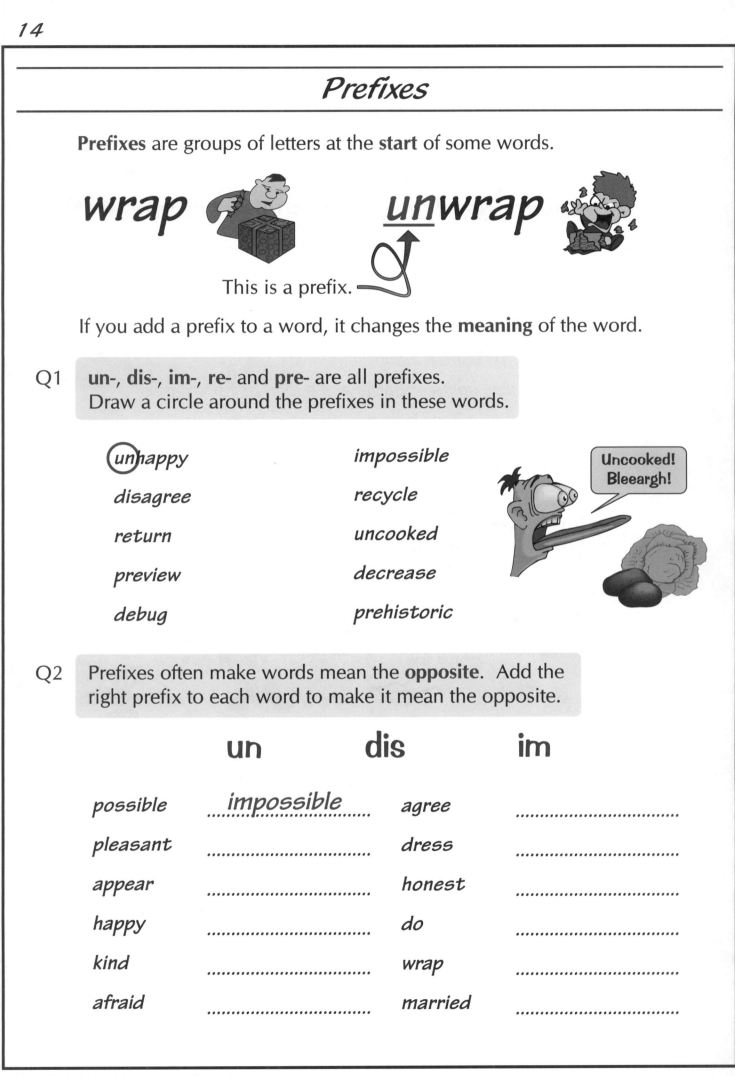 <u>un</u>wrap

This is a prefix.

If you add a prefix to a word, it changes the **meaning** of the word.

Q1 **un-**, **dis-**, **im-**, **re-** and **pre-** are all prefixes.
Draw a circle around the prefixes in these words.

(un)happy   *impossible*

disagree   *recycle*

return   *uncooked*

preview   *decrease*

debug   *prehistoric*

Uncooked!
Bleeargh!

Q2 Prefixes often make words mean the **opposite**. Add the
right prefix to each word to make it mean the opposite.

un   dis   im

	un		dis	im
possible	impossible	*agree*	....	....
pleasant	....	*dress*	....	....
appear	....	*honest*	....	....
happy	....	*do*	....	....
kind	....	*wrap*	....	....
afraid	....	*married*	....	....

Prefixes

The prefix **re-** before a word often means **again**.

Q3 Fill in the missing words below. They all begin with **re-**.

.......**repay**....... *to pay again*

.... *to appear again*

.... *to do something again*

.... *to launch again*

The prefix **pre-** often means **before**.

Q4 Fill in the missing words or what they mean.
They all begin with **pre-**.

.......**preview**....... *to view something before*

.... *to pay in advance*

pre-wash ....

pre-cook ....

.... *the time before recorded history.*

Q5 Choose the best prefix to complete each of these words.

.......**un**....... tie *to undo a knot*

.... usual *strange, not usual*

.... true *not correct or true*

.... polite *rude, not polite*

.... arrange *to arrange something again*

.... heated *heated in advance*

Synonyms

Synonyms are words which mean the same thing.

big   huge

These two words are **synonyms**.

jump   leap   spring

These are synonyms, **too**.

Q1 Draw lines to join up the words which mean the same thing.

big   little

small   tidy

happy   adore

smell   cheerful

neat   stink

love   huge

Q2 Finish off the sentences using the words in the box.

> twist   dirty   shake
> horrible   terrible   wet   ~~cold~~

Freezing means the same as ...... *cold* ......

Damp means the same as ....

Nasty means the same as ....

Rattle means the same as ....

Bad means the same as ....

Filthy means the same as ....

Turn means the same as ....

Synonyms

Q3 Look at these pairs of words.
Put circles around the ones which are synonyms.

(sack
bag)

sea
ocean

soup
horse

football
bus

street
road

lorry
truck

pig
hog

car
water

chair
table

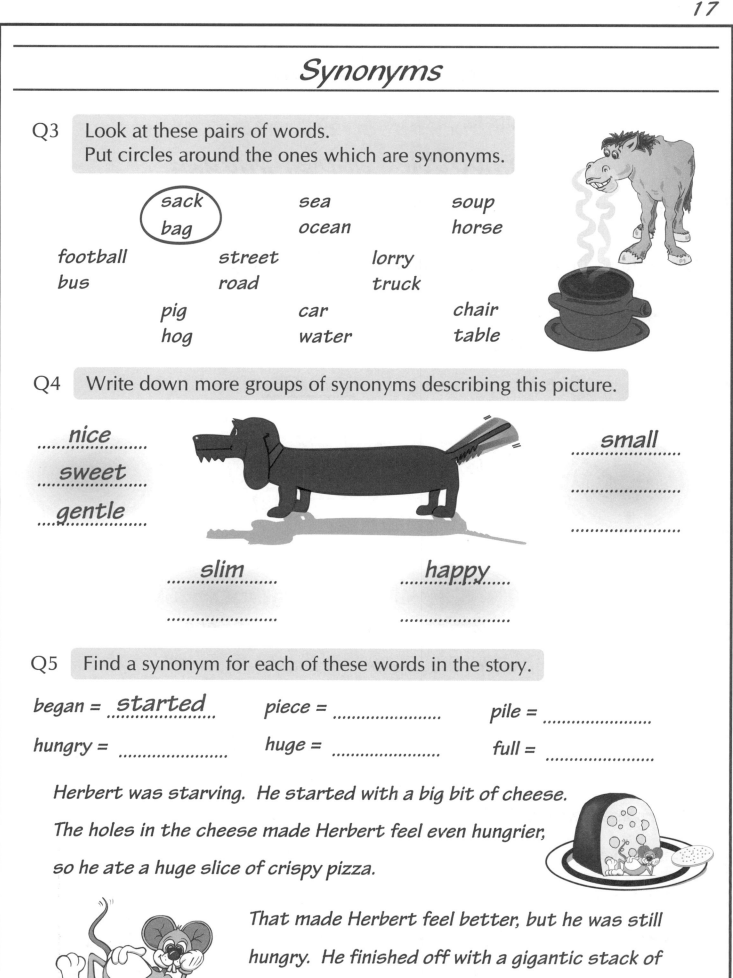

Q4 Write down more groups of synonyms describing this picture.

nice

sweet

gentle

small

slim

happy

Q5 Find a synonym for each of these words in the story.

began = started

piece = ...

pile = ...

hungry = ...

huge = ...

full = ...

Herbert was starving. He started with a big bit of cheese.

The holes in the cheese made Herbert feel even hungrier,

so he ate a huge slice of crispy pizza.

That made Herbert feel better, but he was still

hungry. He finished off with a gigantic stack of

pancakes and jam. Now he was really stuffed.

Words Ending with '-le'

These words end with **-le**.

little bottle apple bubble

There are lots more words that end with **-le**.

Q1 Fill in the letters to give the names of these things.

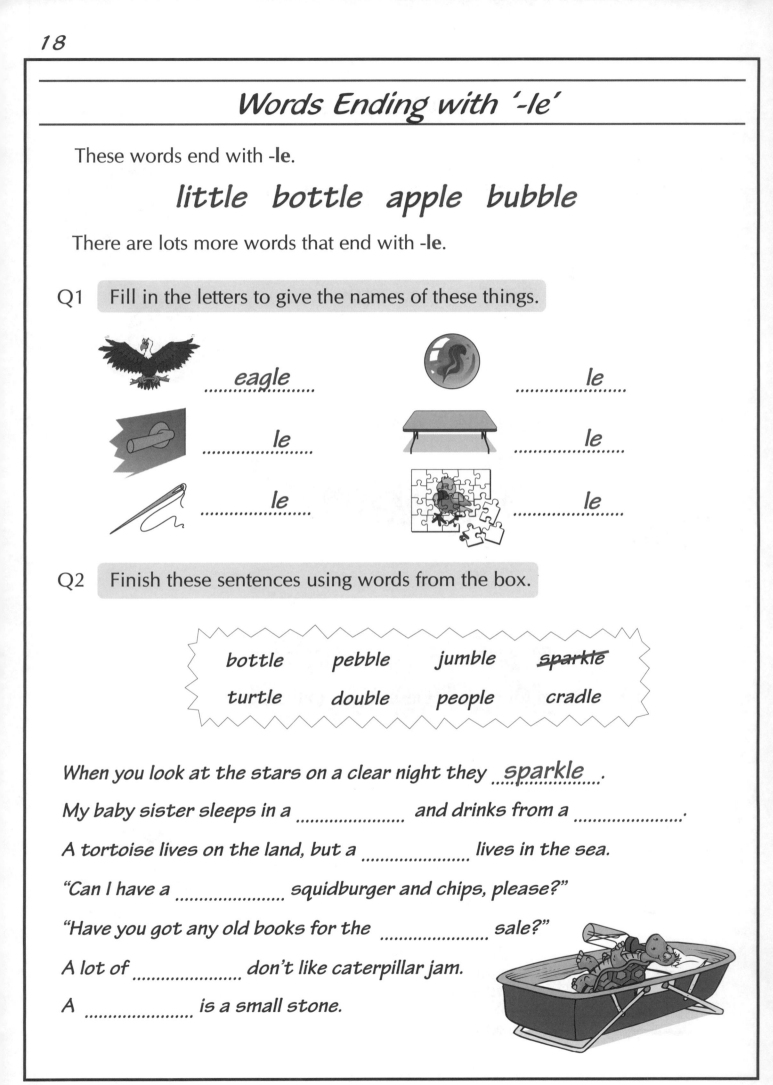

.......*eagle*.......   .... **le**

.... **le**   .... **le**

.... **le**   .... **le**

Q2 Finish these sentences using words from the box.

> bottle   pebble   jumble   ~~sparkle~~
>
> turtle   double   people   cradle

When you look at the stars on a clear night they ...*sparkle*... .

My baby sister sleeps in a .... and drinks from a ....

A tortoise lives on the land, but a .... lives in the sea.

"Can I have a .... squidburger and chips, please?"

"Have you got any old books for the .... sale?"

A lot of .... don't like caterpillar jam.

A .... is a small stone.

Silent Letters

Some words have **silent letters** in them.

carve gnome hour
whisper knife wrist

You can't **hear** the silent letter when you say the word.

Q1   Write down the silent letters in each of these words.

bite   ....e............   whole   ......w..... , ...e.....

sign   ....   knit   ....

wrap   ....   knock   ....

whip   ....   wrinkle   .... , ...

what   ....   wrong   ....

Q2   Fill in the missing silent letters using the clues below.

k.....nuckle   w.....ite   .....naw   .....onest   .....rite

.....riggle   snak.....   .....hole   r.....inoceros   .....nife

What missing letters?

Adding '-y' to Words

You can add **-y** to the end of some words to make new words.

chew ➡ chewy

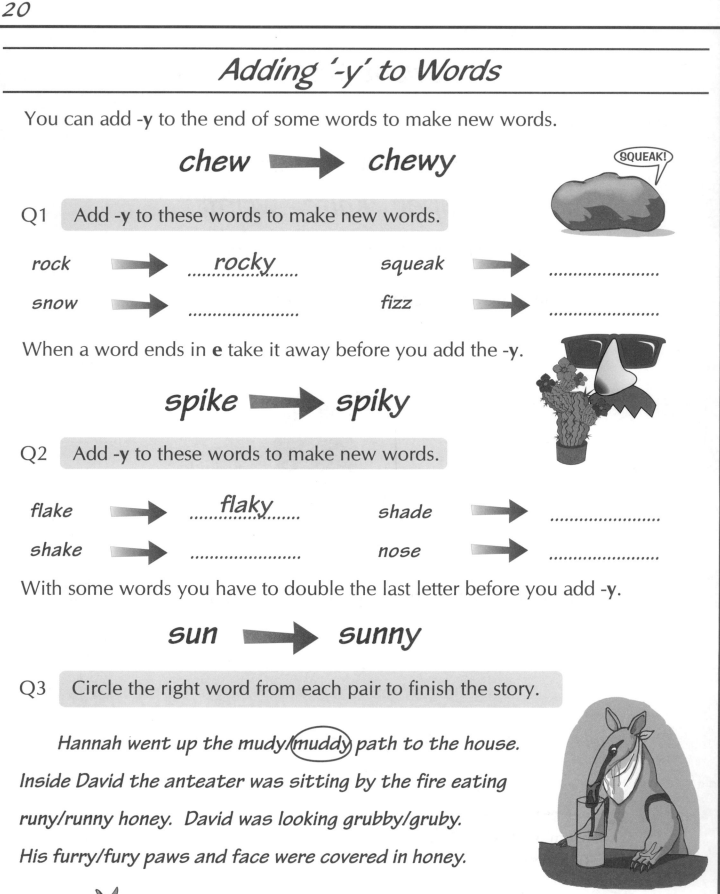

Q1 Add **-y** to these words to make new words.

rock ➡ ....rocky.......   squeak ➡ ....

snow ➡ ....   fizz ➡ ....

When a word ends in **e** take it away before you add the **-y**.

spike ➡ spiky

Q2 Add **-y** to these words to make new words.

flake ➡ ......flaky......   shade ➡ ....

shake ➡ ....   nose ➡ ....

With some words you have to double the last letter before you add **-y**.

sun ➡ sunny

Q3 Circle the right word from each pair to finish the story.

Hannah went up the mudy/(muddy) path to the house.

Inside David the anteater was sitting by the fire eating

runy/runny honey. David was looking grubby/gruby.

His furry/fury paws and face were covered in honey.

David gave Hannah a jar of honey. The jar was long and

skiny/skinny. Hannah couldn't get her stuby/stubby

nose into the jar. David thought it was very funny/funy.

Adding '-er' and '-est' to Words

You can add -**er** and -**est** to many words to make new words.

taller older widest ←

The **e** at the end of wide turns into the **e** in -**est**.

When you add -**er** and -**est** to a word ending in -**y**, the **y** changes to **i**.

smelly → *smellier, smelliest*

Q1 Fill in the gaps in the wall before it falls down.

small	*smaller*	smallest
light	lighter	....
nasty	....	nastiest
low	lower	....
dark	....	darkest
funny	....	funniest
cold	colder	....
warm	....	....
dry	drier	....

Q2 Double the last letter of these words before adding -**er** and -**est**.

	-er	-est
big	*bigger*	*biggest*
fat	....	....
hot	....	....
fit	....	....
thin	....	....
wet	....	....

Singulars and Plurals

A word about one thing is called a **singular**.
A word about more than one thing is called a **plural**. It ends in **-s**.

pigs   engines   parks

Q1 Add **-s** to these words to make them plural.

house.......... lamp.......... card.......... drum..........

Q2 Put a ring around all the words which are about more than one thing.

Look out — two of these words are singulars, even though they end in -s.

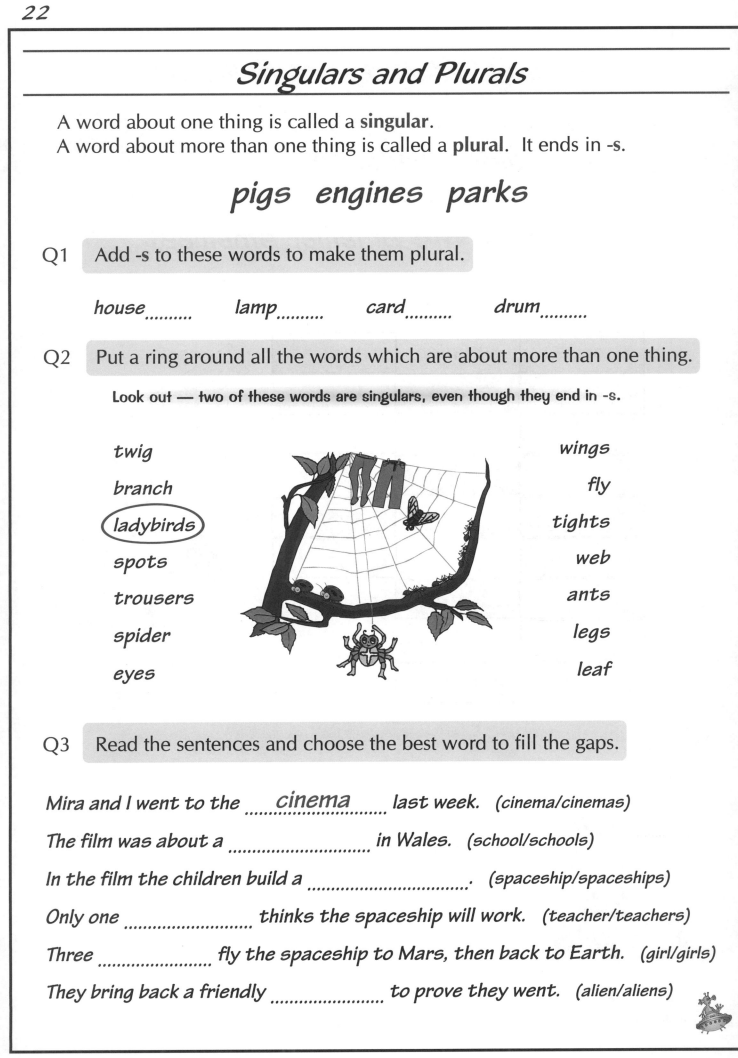

twig

branch

(ladybirds)

spots

trousers

spider

eyes

wings

fly

tights

web

ants

legs

leaf

Q3 Read the sentences and choose the best word to fill the gaps.

Mira and I went to the ....cinema........... last week. (cinema/cinemas)

The film was about a .... in Wales. (school/schools)

In the film the children build a .... (spaceship/spaceships)

Only one .... thinks the spaceship will work. (teacher/teachers)

Three .... fly the spaceship to Mars, then back to Earth. (girl/girls)

They bring back a friendly .... to prove they went. (alien/aliens)

Singulars and Plurals

Some words sound wrong if you just add **-s**.
You need **-es** to make them plural.

classes   matches   foxes

Most words ending in **-o** just need an **-s** for the plural, but these ones need **-es**:

tomatoes   volcanoes   echoes   heroes

Q4 Add **-s** or **-es** to make these words plural.

peach ..es.........   piano ....

table ..s..........   dish ....

car ....   wheel ....

dress ....   box ....

switch ....   potato ....

With words ending in **-y**, check which letter comes before the **y**.
If it's a **consonant**, change the **y** to **ie** before adding **s**.

Vowels are a, e, i, o, and u. *Consonants* are all the other letters.

memory ➡ memories

Q5 Put a tick or a cross to show whether the plurals are right or wrong.
If they are wrong, write them out properly at the bottom of the page.

☑ jelly — jellies   ☐ valley — valleys

☐ fly — flies   ☐ boy — boys

☐ puppy — puppys   ☐ chimney — chimneies

☐ baby — babys

....

Compound Words

Compound words are made by adding together two other words.

$$tea + pot \longrightarrow teapot$$

Q1 Add these words together to make some compound words.

tooth + brush = <u>toothbrush</u>

rain + coat = ...

bed + room = ...

dish + cloth = ...

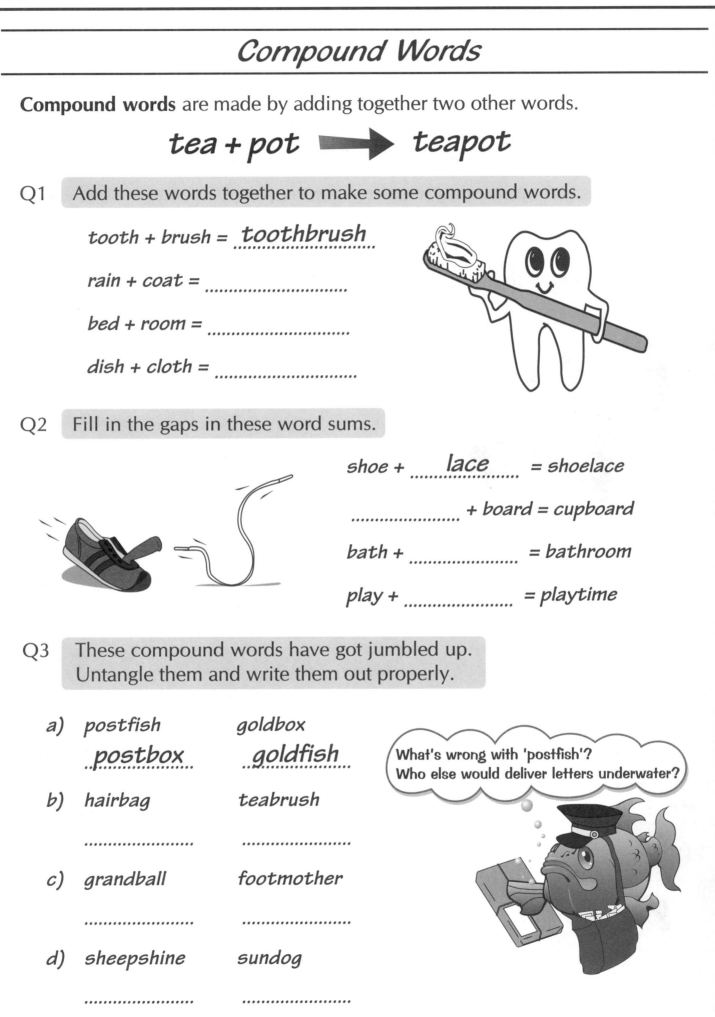

Q2 Fill in the gaps in these word sums.

shoe + <u>lace</u> = shoelace

.... + board = cupboard

bath + ... = bathroom

play + ... = playtime

Q3 These compound words have got jumbled up.
Untangle them and write them out properly.

a) postfish   goldbox

<u>postbox</u>   <u>goldfish</u>

b) hairbag   teabrush

....

c) grandball   footmother

....

d) sheepshine   sundog

....

What's wrong with 'postfish'?
Who else would deliver letters underwater?

Compound Words

Q4 Use these words to make compound words and label the drawing. You might have to use some of the words more than once.

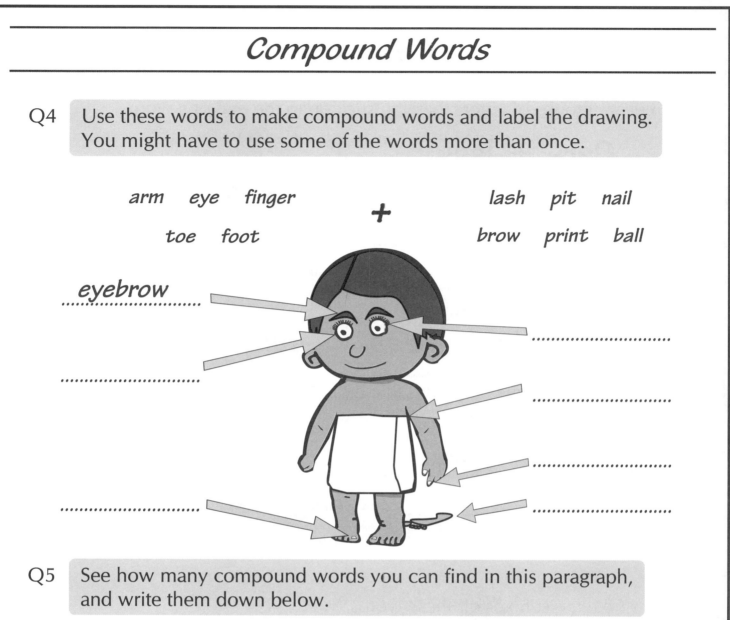

arm   eye   finger
toe   foot

+

lash   pit   nail
brow   print   ball

eyebrow
....

....

....

....

....

....

....

Q5 See how many compound words you can find in this paragraph, and write them down below.

My grandmother is very kind, but a bit weird.

She always wears a raincoat, even when there's lots

of sunshine. She doesn't drink tea out of a teacup.

Instead she uses a saucepan or a flowerpot.

Grandma has got a pet blackbird, and

she takes it around town on a birdcage.

grandmother   ....

....

....

Suffixes

Suffixes are groups of letters that you stick on to the **end** of a word.

Care + less

→ Care**less**

This part is the suffix

These are some important suffixes.

-ly   -ness   -ful   -less

Q1 Suffixes change one word into a different word.
Make each word into a new word by adding the suffixes.

real + ly ....really....... help + ful ....

care + ful .... power + less ....

dark + ness .... mad + ly ....

Q2 Take the suffixes off these words.
Write the word that's left.

hopeful ....hope.... sadly ....

differently .... goodness ....

thoughtless .... colourful ....

Q3 If the word ends in **-y**, change this to **i** before you add the suffix **-ly**.
Add **-ly** to these words to make new words.

happy ....happily.... Boo

busy ....

pretty .... scary ....

Suffixes

You can sometimes add **-er** to the end of a doing word to make a person word.

Q4   Make these doing words into people words.

hunt	....hunter....	teach	....
work	....	help	....
sing	....	walk	....
golf	....	think	....
bank	....	preach	....

Careful — not all person words end in **-er**.
Some end in **-or**.

Inventor   **Actor**   **Sailor**

Q5   Use these suffixes to make new words. You can
sometimes make more than one new word.

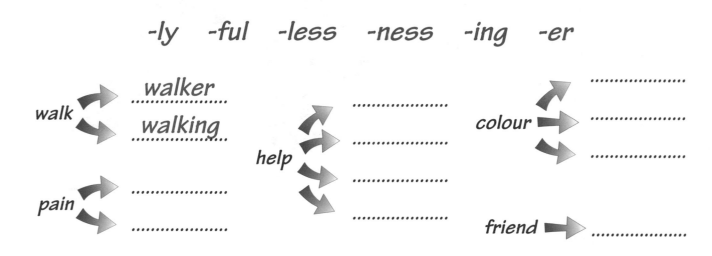

-ly   -ful   -less   -ness   -ing   -er

walk → *walker*
       walking

pain → ....
       ....

help → ....
       ....
       ....
       ....

colour → ....
         ....
         ....

friend → ....

Confusing Words

Some words are confusing because they sound the same as other words.

 I write with my right hand.

These two words sound the

same, but they look different

and mean different things.

Q1 Link each word on the left to one that sounds the same.

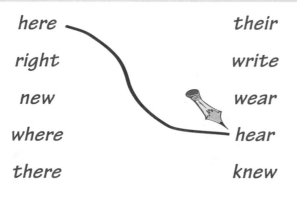

here	their
right	write
new	wear
where	hear
there	knew

Q2 Find three pairs of words that sound the same in this sentence but which aren't spelt the same. Write your words in the spaces below.

No, I don't know which witch would cast spells in the wood at night.

1.   *no*
....
      know
....

2. ....
....

3. ....
....

Confusing Words

Q3   Choose the right word for each gap.

He planted the tree in a (whole / hole) ___hole___.

Oops. I'm an (hour / our) _____ late.

Speak louder. I can't (hear / here) _____ you.

I can't do this (some / sum) _____. It's too hard.

Q4   Use the help on the left to choose either **two**, **too** or **to** for each gap.
Remember that they all mean different things.

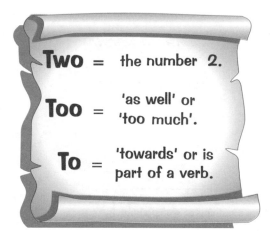

Two = the number **2**.

Too = 'as well' or 'too much'.

To = 'towards' or is part of a verb.

I've got (~~too~~ / to / two) much homework for

Maths, and for English (too / to / two).

The English teacher wants us (too / to / two)

write (too / to / two) stories before

tomorrow, but I'd prefer (too / to / two) go

(too / to / two) the football match instead.

Q5   One word in each line is wrong and is coloured **blue**.
Write what it should be on the dots.

She nose how to speak French.   ___knows___

Right me a letter when you arrive.   _____

I don't no where he lives.   _____

Wear would you like to live?   _____

I think I wood like to visit France.   _____

Confusing Words

Raw meat →

Roar meat ←

Apostrophes

Use an **apostrophe** to show where you've left letters out.

Leave out the 'a'...

I am

...and put an apostrophe instead.

I'm

Leave out these 4 letters...

She would

...and add 1 apostrophe.

She'd

Q1 Leave out the **red** letters and use an apostrophe to make these phrases shorter.

we are	*we're*	they are	....
she is	....	Sue is	....
I will	....	we had	....
you have	....	Jim will	....

Q2 Shorten each of these sentences by writing the short versions of the words in **blue**.

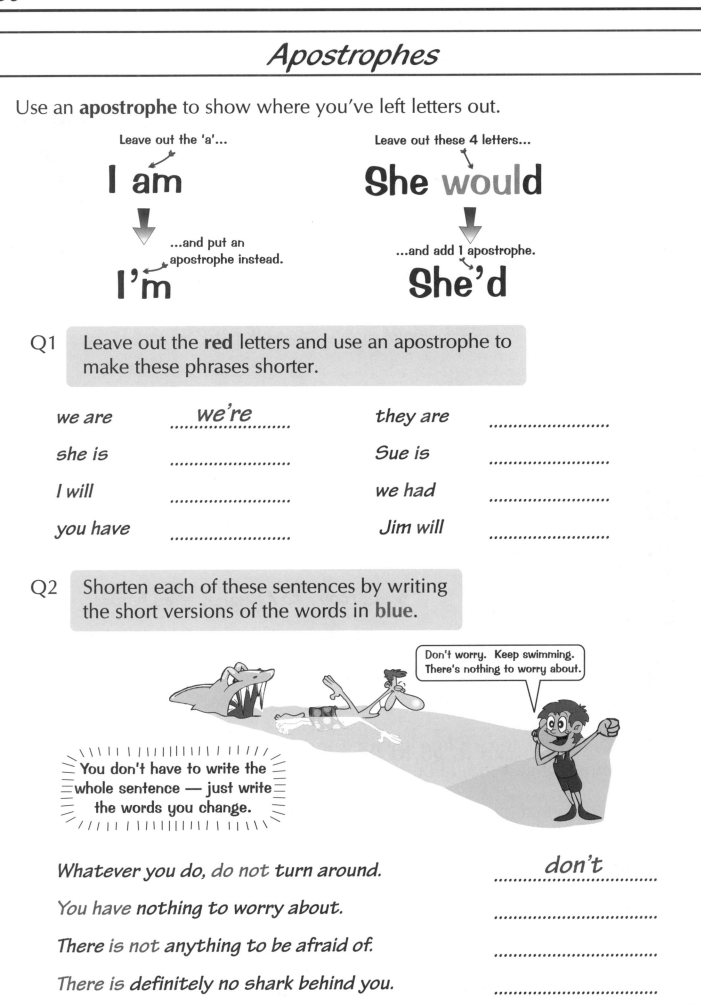

Don't worry. Keep swimming. There's nothing to worry about.

You don't have to write the whole sentence — just write the words you change.

Whatever you do, do not turn around.   *don't*

You have nothing to worry about.   ....

There is not anything to be afraid of.   ....

There is definitely no shark behind you.   ....

Apostrophes

Q3 Write the long versions of these words.
Sometimes you need to add more than one letter.

you're   ....you are....   STRETCH   we've   ....

I'm   ....   didn't   ....

isn't   ....   wouldn't   ....

Q4   Put the apostrophes in these sentences.

> You'll need to add 2 apostrophes to the last sentence.

Whos knocking at the door?

Theres someone here to speak to you.

I dont want to speak to him.

I dont think hell take no for an answer.

Careful: sometimes an apostrophe can mean more than one thing.

She'd gone to the shops.   She'd = She had

She'd like to go to the shops.   She'd = She would

Q5   Write what the words in **blue** in these sentences mean.

Tim's seeing the film this afternoon.   ....

Tim's seen the film before.   ....

I'd just finished cooking when disaster struck.   ....

I'd rather finish this before we go out.   ....

Definitions

A **definition** tells you what a word means.

guitar   a musical instrument with strings across it that you play with your fingers.

This is the **definition** — it tells you what a guitar is in easy words.

Q1   Draw a line between these 4 words and their definitions.

present

a ship that can travel underwater.

lighthouse

a thing you use to speak to someone who is a long way away.

telephone

a tower with a bright light that warns ships of rocks or other dangers.

submarine

something you give to or get from someone.

Definitions are what you find in a **dictionary**.

Q2   Draw a circle around the words that are with the right definitions.

yoghurt

a thick liquid made from milk. You eat it with a spoon.

point

the sharp end of something.

report

a machine in a factory controlled by a computer.

melon

a long fruit with a thick, yellow skin.

nightmare

a frightening dream.

hand

the part of the body at the end of your arm.

exercise

work that makes your body healthy and strong.

mermaid

someone who lives next door to you or near you.

thunder

the bright light that flashes in the sky during a storm.

Definitions

Q3 There is a mistake in each of these definitions.
Circle the mistake and write what it should be.

dolphin an animal with warm blood that lives in (trees)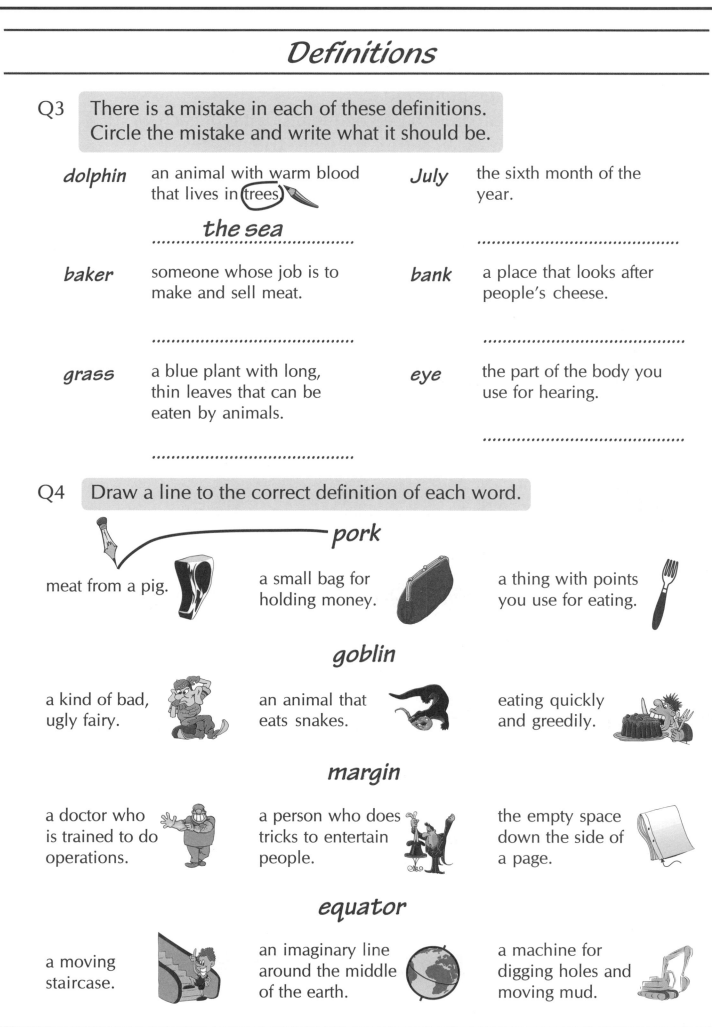

the sea
....

July the sixth month of the year.

....

baker someone whose job is to make and sell meat.

....

bank a place that looks after people's cheese.

....

grass a blue plant with long, thin leaves that can be eaten by animals.

....

eye the part of the body you use for hearing.

....

Q4 Draw a line to the correct definition of each word.

pork

meat from a pig.

a small bag for holding money.

a thing with points you use for eating.

goblin

a kind of bad, ugly fairy.

an animal that eats snakes.

eating quickly and greedily.

margin

a doctor who is trained to do operations.

a person who does tricks to entertain people.

the empty space down the side of a page.

equator

a moving staircase.

an imaginary line around the middle of the earth.

a machine for digging holes and moving mud.

34

Alphabetical Order

These words have been put in order.
They're in alphabetical order based on the first letter of each word.

<u>d</u>og <u>e</u>ngine <u>m</u>achine <u>t</u>ape

Q1 Put each of these lists of words into alphabetical order.
Remember to use the first letter of each word.

a) sausage, cake, toffee, margarine

....

b) sleep, none, coffee, dawn

....

c) mountain, eggs, snake, rhubarb

....

d) pipe, flute, drum, banjo

....

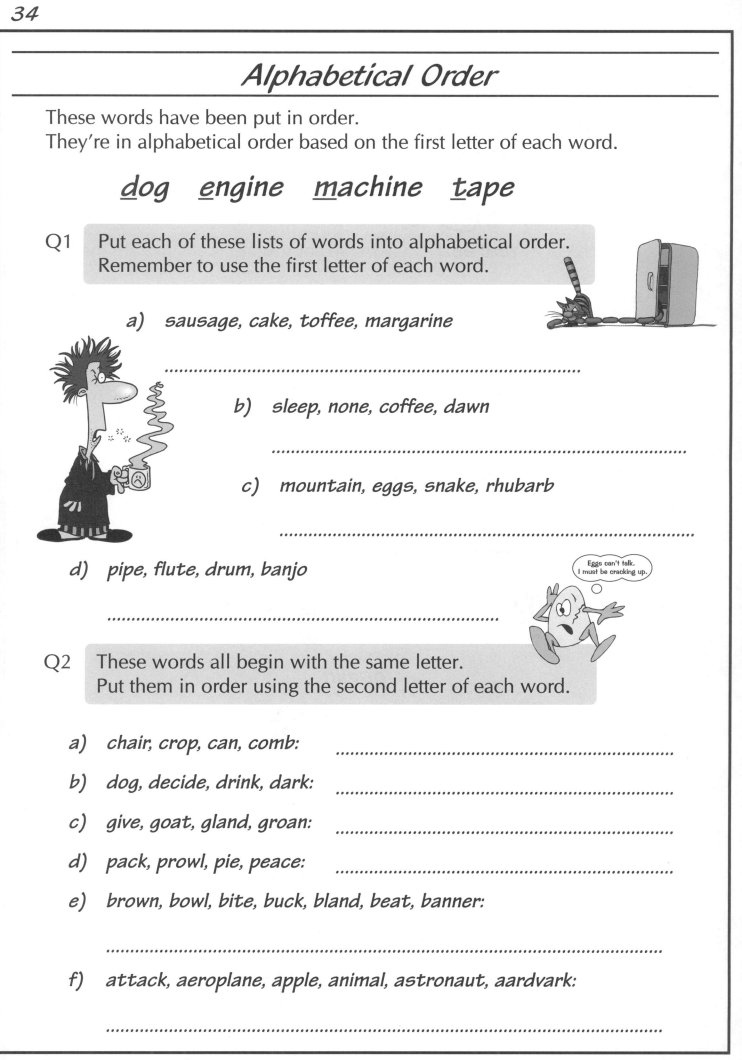

Eggs can't talk. I must be cracking up.

Q2 These words all begin with the same letter.
Put them in order using the second letter of each word.

a) chair, crop, can, comb: ....

b) dog, decide, drink, dark: ....

c) give, goat, gland, groan: ....

d) pack, prowl, pie, peace: ....

e) brown, bowl, bite, buck, bland, beat, banner:

....

f) attack, aeroplane, apple, animal, astronaut, aardvark:

....

Spelling — Internal Words

Here's a good trick to help you with your spelling.
A lot of long words have short words hidden inside them.

many ➡ man + any

Q1 Match each word on the left with a short word that's hidden inside it.

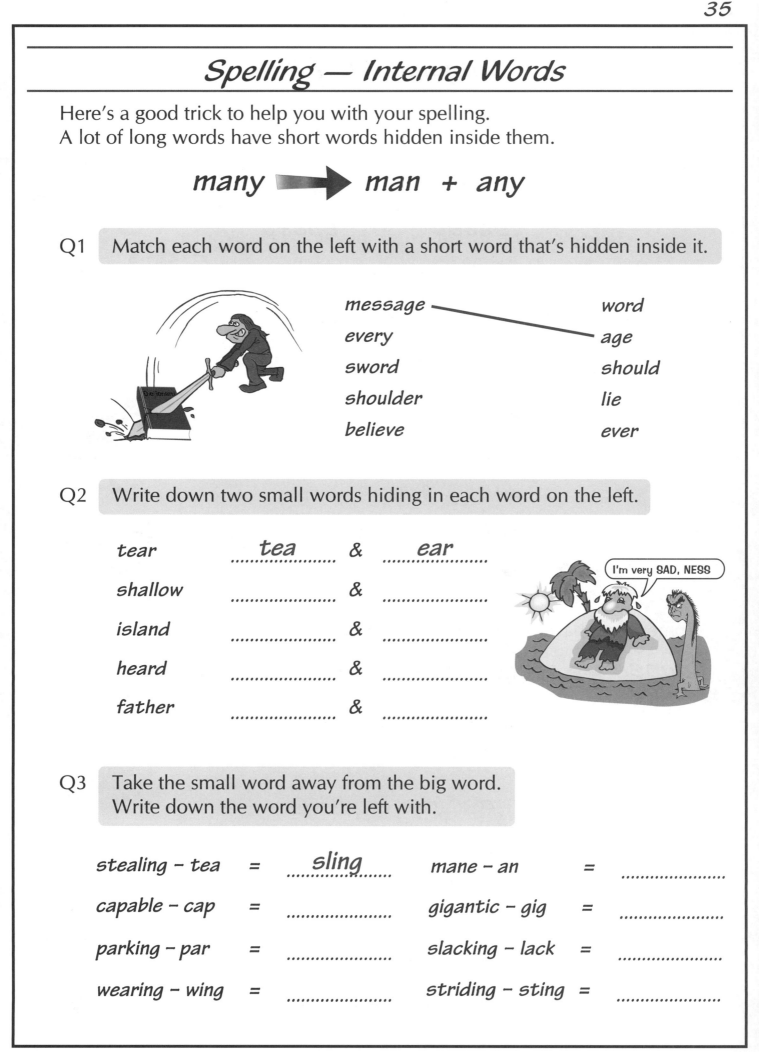

message	word
every	age
sword	should
shoulder	lie
believe	ever

Q2 Write down two small words hiding in each word on the left.

tear	_tea_	&	_ear_
shallow	....	&	....
island	....	&	....
heard	....	&	....
father	....	&	....

I'm very SAD, NESS

Q3 Take the small word away from the big word.
Write down the word you're left with.

stealing – tea	=	_sling_	mane – an	=	....
capable – cap	=	....	gigantic – gig	=	....
parking – par	=	....	slacking – lack	=	....
wearing – wing	=	....	striding – sting	=	....

Singular and Plural

Usually you add an '**-s**' or '**-es**' to turn a singular word into a plural.
But some words don't change at all.

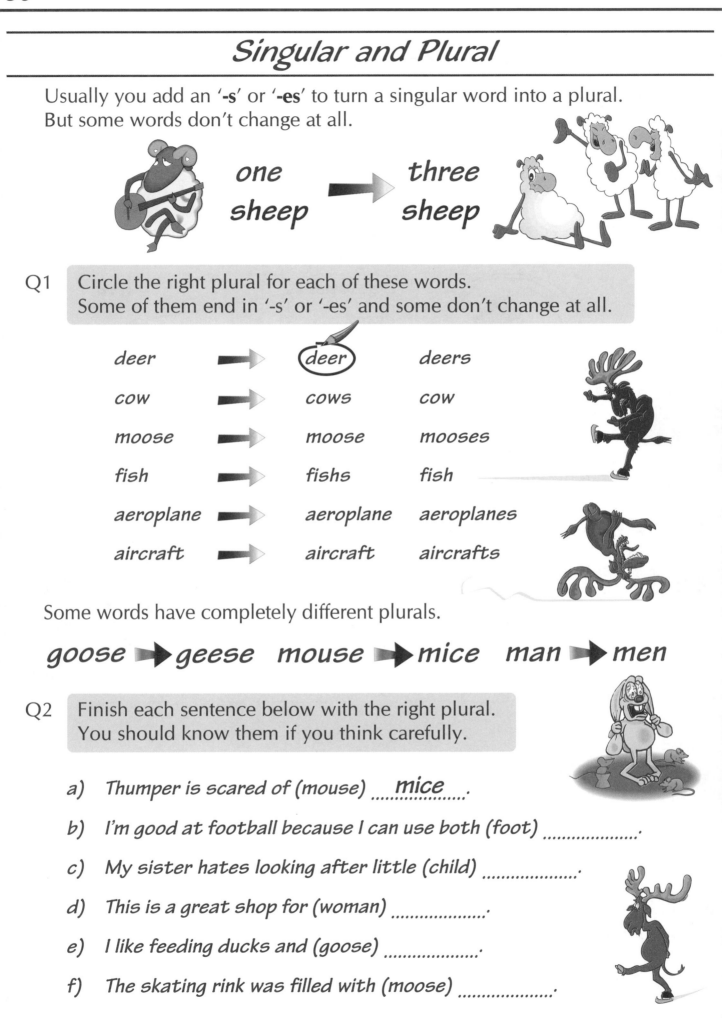

one sheep ➡ three sheep

Q1 Circle the right plural for each of these words.
Some of them end in '-s' or '-es' and some don't change at all.

deer ➡ (deer)   deers

cow ➡ cows   cow

moose ➡ moose   mooses

fish ➡ fishs   fish

aeroplane ➡ aeroplane   aeroplanes

aircraft ➡ aircraft   aircrafts

Some words have completely different plurals.

goose ➡ geese   mouse ➡ mice   man ➡ men

Q2 Finish each sentence below with the right plural.
You should know them if you think carefully.

a) Thumper is scared of (mouse) ..... *mice* .....

b) I'm good at football because I can use both (foot) ....

c) My sister hates looking after little (child) ....

d) This is a great shop for (woman) ....

e) I like feeding ducks and (goose) ....

f) The skating rink was filled with (moose) ....

Singular and Plural

Most words ending in an '-**f**' sound have a different plural.
The plural ends in '-**ves**'.

shelf ➡ **shelves**

thief ➡ **thieves**

Q3 Change these words from singular to plural.

calf ......*calves*......   leaf ....

loaf ....   elf ....

knife ....   scarf ....

A few words don't change the '-**f**'. Instead they just add '-**s**'.

chief ➡ **chiefs**

Q4 Circle the right plural for each of the words below.

belief ➡ (beliefs) believes   proof ➡ proofs prooves

roof ➡ rooves roofs   reef ➡ reefs reeves

Q5 Look at the paragraph below.
Put the right plural in each of the gaps.

Amy shivered. Behind her she heard lots of (wolf) ......*wolves*...... howling. Up ahead in the distance, she saw the (roof) .... of the houses in the village. Not far to go now. She wrapped both her (scarf) .... around her and prayed there weren't any (thief) .... hiding in the bushes. She didn't want anyone to steal all her (loaf) .... of bread.

38

Opposites

Look at these words. They're pairs of opposites.

love ▶ *hate*   *bad* ▶ *good*   *happy* ▶ *sad*

Q1 Match each word on the left with its opposite on the right.

buy	full
lose	small
big	sell
empty	rough
smooth	win

Win

Honestly, it's the taking part that counts.

Lose

But, I have to win. I must win. I always win.

Q2 Circle the word that means the opposite of the one on the left.

soft	kind	(hard)	fine
true	weak	sad	false
old	young	nice	well
heavy	wild	cheap	light
remember	help	forget	borrow

Q3 Look at the sentences below. The key word is marked for you. Change the key word so the sentence means the opposite.

a) Helen is always *nasty* to gerbils.

....

b) Boris was wearing a *new* wig.

....

c) Martin has *filled* his lunch box.

....

Opposites

Q4 Fill the gaps in each sentence with two sensible words from the list.
Then write the sentence out using the opposites of both words.

a) I'm always _happy_ when United _lose_.

strange, ugly, happy, eat, lose

I'm always sad when United win.

b) The dinosaur's skin was .... and its teeth were ....

sharp, tasty, kind, rough, cheap

DADDY

....

....

c) Robin Hood stole from the .... to give to the ....

sheep, rich, snails, poor, stupid

....

Q5 Read this paragraph, then use the list below to change
each of the pink words to its opposite.
Write it out again. It will sound very different.

Robin Hood
never does
anything for us.

It was bright and warm in the forest. The air was clean
and fresh. All around me were small, young trees, and as I
walked along the path I felt brave. I knew I was in a safe place.

old   dark   cold   dangerous
frightened   dirty   big   stale

....

....

....

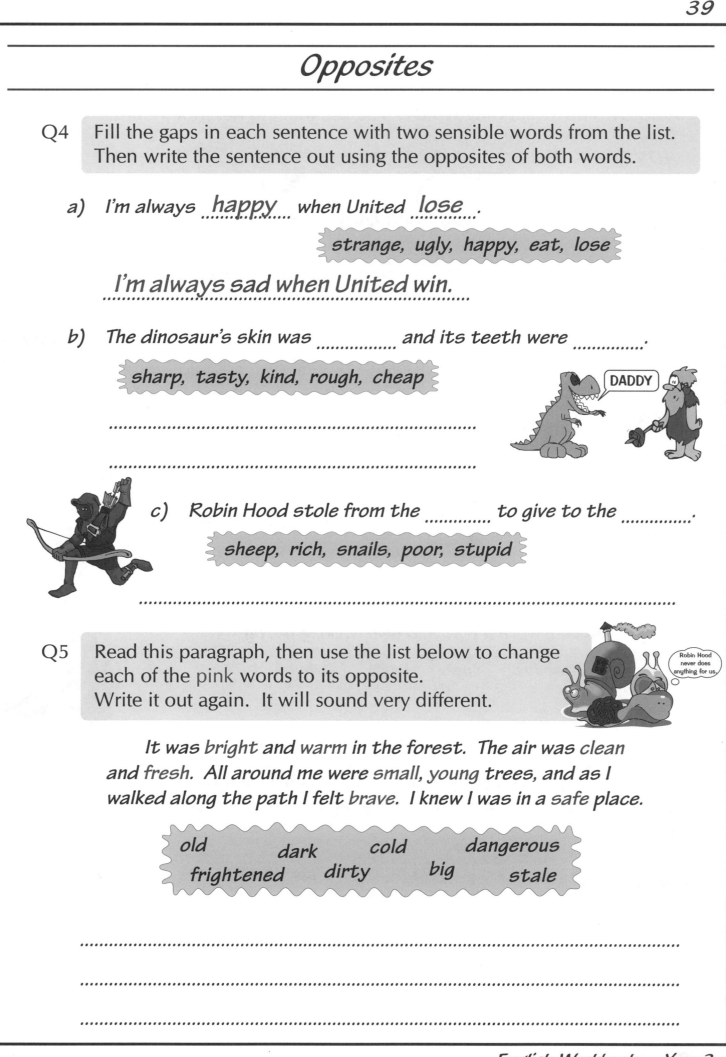

Adjectives

Adjectives are describing words. You use them to describe nouns.
They say what the noun is like.

These words are adjectives.

A fat cat.   A beautiful day.   A kind, old lady.

Q1 Adjectives make sentences more interesting. Make these sentences match the pictures by adding the right adjectives from the list.

a)   The thief climbed in through the window.

cunning   long
green   open

The cunning thief climbed in through the open window.

b)   The spider had eight legs and wore a hat and pullover.

hairy   fast   slimy
wriggly   stripy

....

c)   The man wore a suit and was walking a frog.

smart   ginger   fluffy   green

....

Q2 Here's part of a story with all the adjectives left out.
Fill in the gaps with the right adjectives from the box.

worried   ~~big~~   fierce
brave   terrified

The tiger was _big_ and looked very .... Sam was ....
and ran away screaming. Emily decided to be ...., even though
she was .... She went up to it and said, "Good Kitty!"

Adjectives

Adjectives can be sorted into different types, like shapes or colours.

A ~~green~~ face.   A ~~blue~~ foot.   Red eyes.

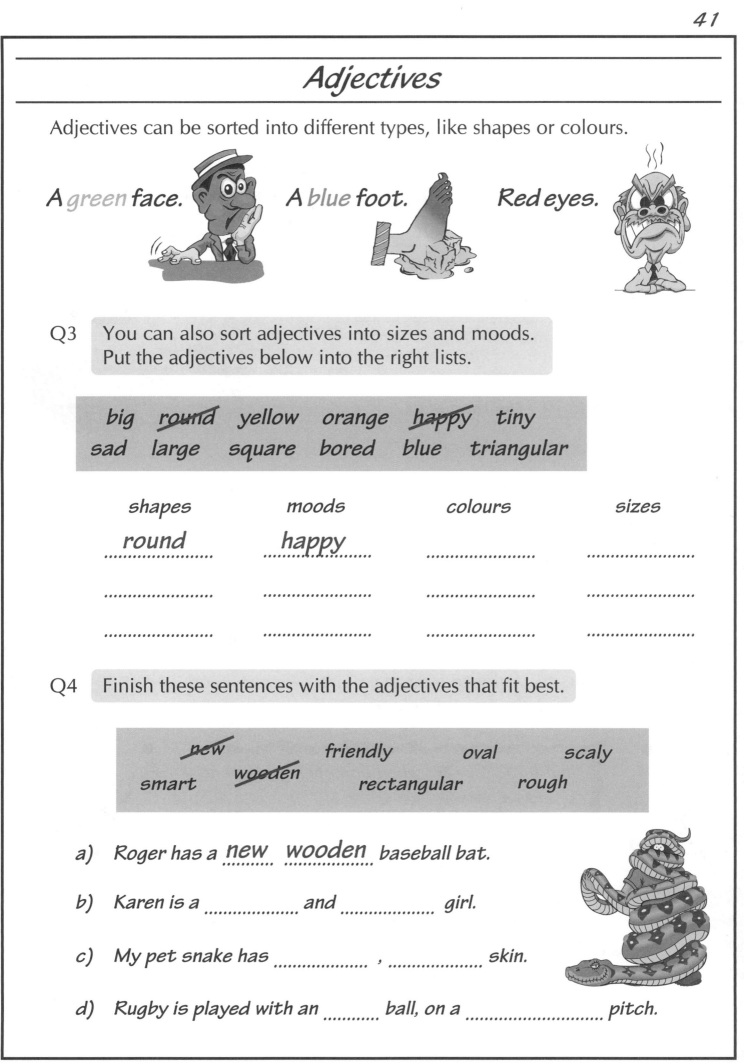

Q3   You can also sort adjectives into sizes and moods.
Put the adjectives below into the right lists.

> big   ~~round~~   yellow   orange   ~~happy~~   tiny
> sad   large   square   bored   blue   triangular

shapes	moods	colours	sizes
round	happy	....	....
....	....	....	....
....	....	....	....

Q4   Finish these sentences with the adjectives that fit best.

> ~~new~~   friendly   oval   scaly
> smart   ~~wooden~~   rectangular   rough

a)   Roger has a <u>new</u> <u>wooden</u> baseball bat.

b)   Karen is a .... and .... girl.

c)   My pet snake has .... , ... skin.

d)   Rugby is played with an .... ball, on a .... pitch.

More Prefixes

Prefixes are groups of letters that go at the **start** of words.

mis + place ➡ *misplace*

Mis means wrong or bad. So misplace means to place something badly.

Q1 Choose the right words from the box to finish the sentences.

~~read~~   take   spell
     treat   judged

Did that sign say "Top end of toad"?

I think you misread, dear.

STOP
END OF ROAD

Paul mis *read* the road sign.

Natalie has made a big mis ....:

Daisy thinks you should never mis .... animals.

James mis .... the distance across the stream.

Steven hates people who mis .... the word 'plesiosaurus'.

The prefix **co-** means **together**.
Words that start **co-** are about two or more things coming together.

Q2 Match the **co-** words to their meanings, using these definitions to help you.

incident ➡ when something happens
operate ➡ work
author ➡ write a book
exist ➡ live

coincidence   live side by side
co-author   work together
coexist   write a book with someone else
cooperate   when two things happen at once

More Prefixes

There are lots of useful words that start with the prefix **ex-**.

Q3   Circle the word in each pair which fits the sentence best.

It's so exhausting spending all day in a museum...

Pinkosaurus minimus

Leo and Justine went to see the dinosaur (exhibition)/ exercise. The exhibition expected/explained how the dinosaurs became expensive/extinct. After looking at all the exhibits/excuses Leo and Justine were expelled/exhausted, but they thought the dinosaurs were excellent/experienced.

Adding these prefixes to words makes them mean the opposite.

anti- + *freeze* ➡️ *antifreeze*
non- + *stick* ➡️ *non-stick*

When you add non- this dash usually stays in the word.

Q4   Add **anti-** or **non-** to the incomplete words to finish the story.

"I'm not going to make it," gasped Travis,

looking down in horror at the bite left by the snake.

" <u>Non</u>sense," said Bridget, "Doctor Little has an

.........dote. We've just got to get you back to the camp."

But I only gave him a wee little kiss.

But she knew they were in trouble. Travis was a

..........-swimmer and the river was flowing too fast.

"Let's go. Leave that bag, it's ....-essential," she ordered. Travis

tried to stand, but the pain in his leg was ....-stop. The

..........biotics were wearing off. He felt dizzy and the world seemed

to be spinning ....clockwise around his head.

Pronouns

A **pronoun** is a word used to stand for another word.

The camel stopped. The camel could see the oasis.
The camel stopped. It could see the oasis.

Q1 Use these pronouns to fill the gaps in the sentences.

we   you   they   I   it   us   ~~she~~

.......**She**....... is a shark.   .... are camels.

"Where am .... ?"

"..................... are in the Sahara desert."

"I want to go to the sea. Where is .... ?"

"..................... are going to the sea. Come with ...."

Q2 Write down what the coloured pronoun in each sentence stands for.

"Can you pass me the hammer?" said Kit.   ....**Kit**.......

"I thought you had it," said Tessa.   ....

"I gave it to you," answered Kit.   ....

"Ask the twins. They might know," Tessa replied.   ....

"We don't know where the hammer is," said the twins.   ....

"Are you sure?" asked Tessa.   ....

"I don't believe them," Kit said to Tessa.   ....

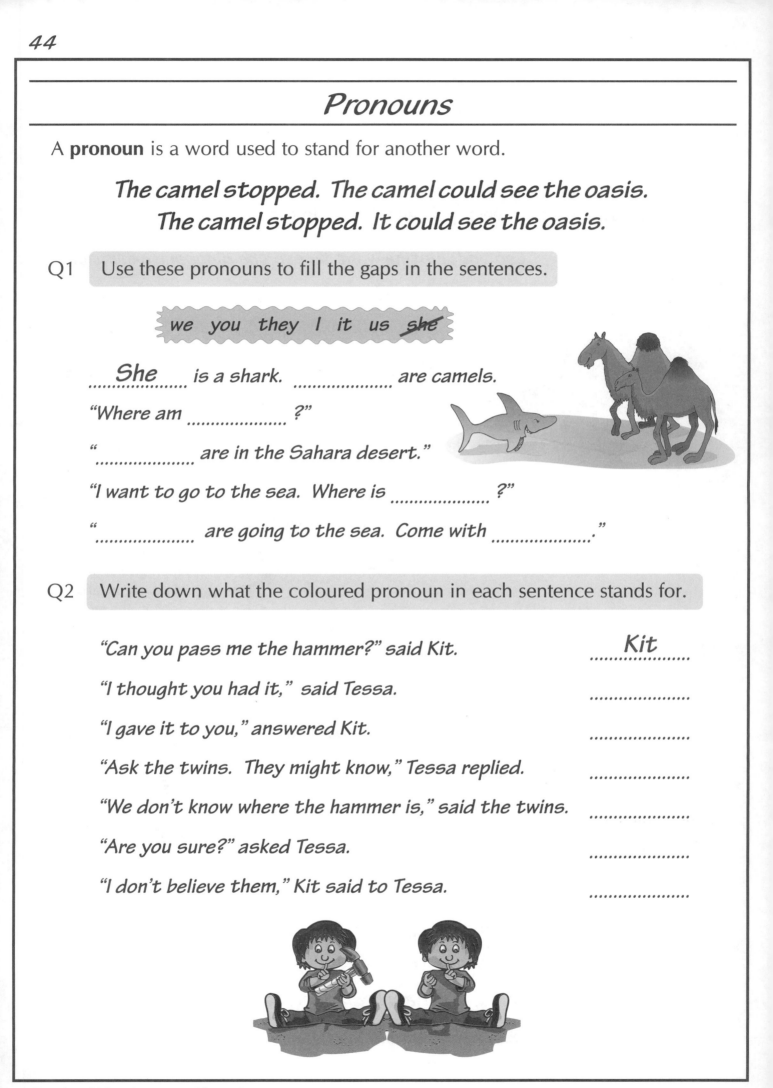

Possessive Pronouns

Some pronouns show who something belongs to.
They are called **possessive pronouns**.

This is my penguin.

The penguin is mine.

Q1   Circle all the words which show who something belongs to.

This is (our) fish tank.

The red fish are his. My fish are yellow.

That is their polar bear tank. The polar bear is theirs.

We think our fish are more beautiful than their bear.

Its fur is a really boring colour.

Q2   Choose a word from the cloud to fill the gaps in each sentence.
You may need to use some words more than once.

theirs   its   hers
my   her   our
his   your   ours

I'm going to take ....my....... umbrella.

Wanda is wearing .... raincoat.

Red Eddy is Gary's goldfish. Red Eddy is ....

Yellow Freddy is Lucy's goldfish. Yellow Freddy is ....

.... penguin is quite a lot bigger than ....

You can't take .... polar bear away from us.

Verbs and Pronouns

Verbs and pronouns have to match.
When the pronoun is **he**, **she** or **it** the verb usually ends in **-s**.

They sleep downstairs.   *He sleeps upstairs.*

sleep matches they   sleeps matches he

Q1   Match the blue pronouns with the verbs in the middle.

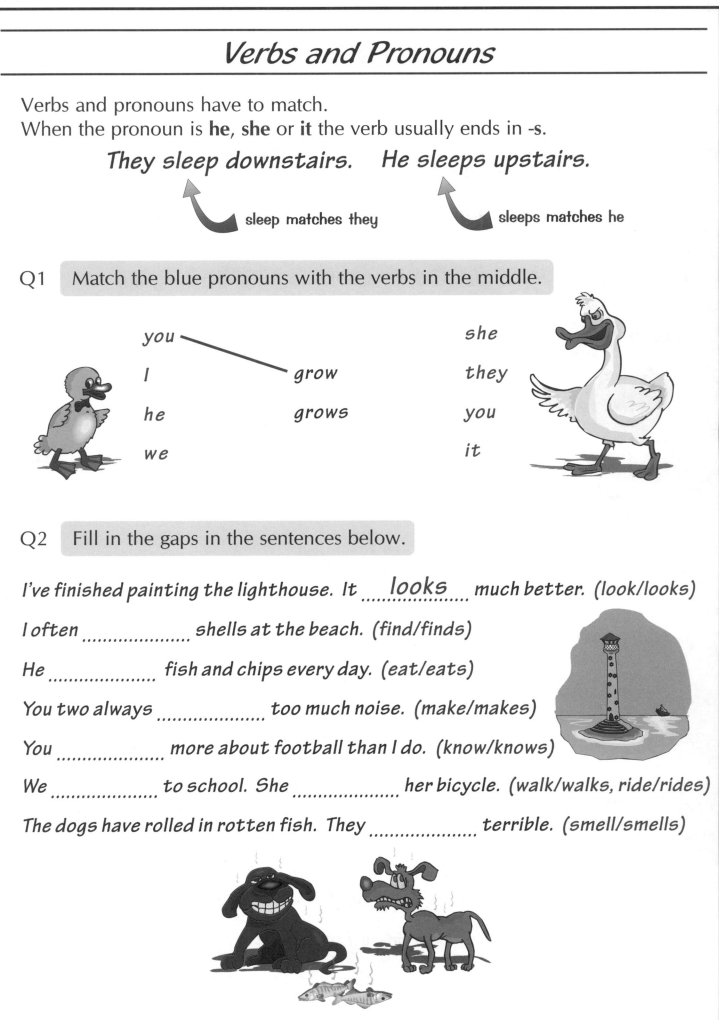

you

I

he

we

grow

grows

she

they

you

it

Q2   Fill in the gaps in the sentences below.

I've finished painting the lighthouse. It ....*looks*.... much better. (look/looks)

I often .... shells at the beach. (find/finds)

He .... fish and chips every day. (eat/eats)

You two always .... too much noise. (make/makes)

You .... more about football than I do. (know/knows)

We .... to school. She .... her bicycle. (walk/walks, ride/rides)

The dogs have rolled in rotten fish. They .... terrible. (smell/smells)

Verbs and Pronouns

The verb **to be** changes more than most words.
You have to be extra careful when you match it to the pronoun.

I	*matches*	*am*
you, we, they	*match*	*are*
he, she, it	*match*	*is*

Q3 Look at the verbs and place them in the sentences.

is He ..... *is* ..... building a space rocket.

are They ..... *are* ..... building a rowing boat.

are It .... fierce and bloodthirsty.

is We .... gentle and quiet.

am I .... going to live in Greece.

is She .... going to live in New York.

am You .... scared.

are I .... terrified.

Q4 In these sentences the pronouns don't match the verbs.
Write the sentences out again with the right verbs.

They is famous pirates.

They are famous pirates. .....

He are going to make us walk the plank.

.....

We buries treasure on islands. Then we forgets where we put it.

.....

She am my parrot. She speak Chinese, English and Spanish.

.....

Plural Sentences

A **singular** sentence is one that's about just **one person or thing**.

I went to the cinema.

The candle went out.

We don't want to go.

They look a bit wet.

If it's about more than one, it's a **plural** sentence.

Q1   Write down if each of these sentences is singular or plural.

I go to school by pogo stick.   ....singular....

Bob just can't stay sitting down.   ....

My cheesecake is full of carrots.   ....

They got a bit wet yesterday.   ....

The bananas are mouldy.   ....

You can change a singular sentence to plural, but you have to be careful. More than one word might change.

I am going home.

We are going home.

Q2   All these sentences are singular. Rewrite them to make them plural.

The girl can really juggle.

The girls can really juggle.

I am feeling very tired.

....

The boy couldn't believe his eyes.

....

English Workbook — Year 3

First, Second and Third Person

If a sentence is written from your point of view, we say it's in the **first person**.

We went to the cinema, after I'd eaten my dinner.

First person sentences often have words like '**I**', '**we**', '**me**' and '**my**'.

If a sentence is only about other people, we say it's in the **third person**.

Claire went out. She was with Tim. They found a huge walrus.

Third person sentences often have words like '**he**', '**she**' and '**they**'.

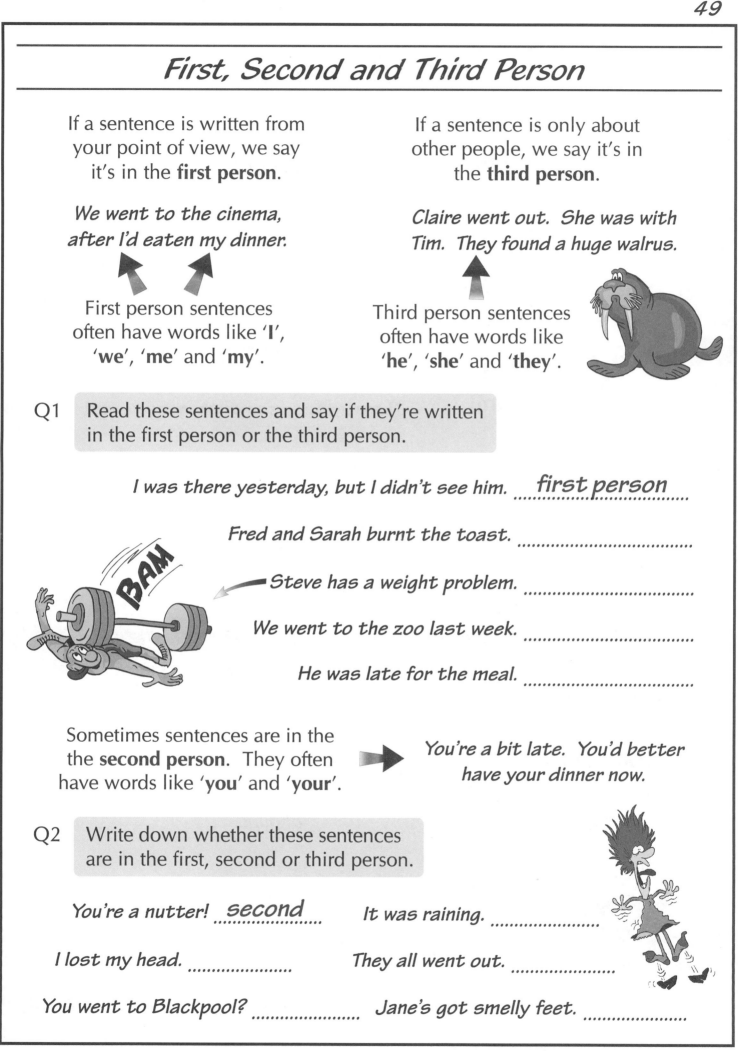

Q1 Read these sentences and say if they're written in the first person or the third person.

I was there yesterday, but I didn't see him. ....first person..........

Fred and Sarah burnt the toast. ....

Steve has a weight problem. ....

We went to the zoo last week. ....

He was late for the meal. ....

Sometimes sentences are in the the **second person**. They often have words like '**you**' and '**your**'.

You're a bit late. You'd better have your dinner now.

Q2 Write down whether these sentences are in the first, second or third person.

You're a nutter! ......second......   *It was raining.* ....

I lost my head. ....   *They all went out.* ....

You went to Blackpool? ....   *Jane's got smelly feet.* ....

Collective Nouns

Collective nouns are words for **groups** of people or things.

What a lovely bunch of flowers!

This is a **collective noun**.

Q1 Circle the collective nouns in these sentences.

What a team!

It was a large (herd) of cattle.

There was a group of them queueing.

I was flattened by a flock of flamingoes.

There was an army of soldiers outside.

Q2 Choose the right collective nouns from the box to complete these sentences.

swarm ~~shoal~~ fleet

team bunch litter

I saw a huge *shoal* of fish in the sea.

What a smelly .... of bananas!

My mad dog had a .... of pups.

There was a big .... of bees in the attic.

A .... of husky dogs was pulling the sled.

The admiral admired his large .... of ships.

Capital Letters

Capital letters aren't just used at the start of a sentence.
People's names always start with a capital letter.

Brian   Wednesday   August

I love these capital letters!

So do days of the week, months of the year, place names and names of things like sports teams.

Q1 Put a circle where there should be a capital letter.

a)   I want to go to ⓐmerica to see ⓓisneyland.

b)   my friend miguel is from spain.

c)   tom's face lit up like a christmas tree.

d)   my friend kirsten says she saw an alien spaceship

on monday night, after eastenders.

Q2 Look at these pairs of sentences. One is right and one is wrong. Put a tick by the correct one.

a)   We're going to scotland at easter.
We're going to Scotland at Easter. ✓

Remember — ordinary words **don't** need a capital letter.

b)   My birthday is in May.
My Birthday is in may.

c)   My friend supports arsenal, but I can't stand Football.
My friend supports Arsenal, but I can't stand football.

Each new line in a poem starts with a capital, even if it's not a new sentence.

Q3 Write this poem out with capital letters in the right places.

Mary had a little fish,
its fins so bright and blue.
She never went out anywhere
if the fish could not go too.

....

....

....

....

Speech

Remember — **speech marks** go around the words that someone says.

Clive said, "That was a bit hot."

↑ When there's no other punctuation, always put a **comma** in these places...

↑ ... and when someone starts speaking, it always starts with a **capital letter**.

"Not half," said Kate.

Q1 Write out these sentences again.
Put in the speech marks, capital letters and commas.

a) *I think I'll skip lunch today said Bob.*

"I think I'll skip lunch today," said Bob.
....

b) *Pam said it looks like it's going to rain.*

....

c) *That can't be right said Sarah.*

....

Use a **question mark** (?) to show when someone's asking a question and an **exclamation mark** (!) when someone's shouting or yelling.

Q2 Put speech marks, question marks and exclamation marks in these sentences.

a) *It's a bit windy yelled Geoffrey.*

"It's a bit windy!" yelled Geoffrey.
....

b) *Where do you think you're going asked Billy's mum.*

....

c) *Is it okay if we teach the dog how to fly asked Billy.*

....

Speech

Don't just use 'said'. Use different words to say how someone's speaking.

Q3 For each picture of Helen, say which word fits best.

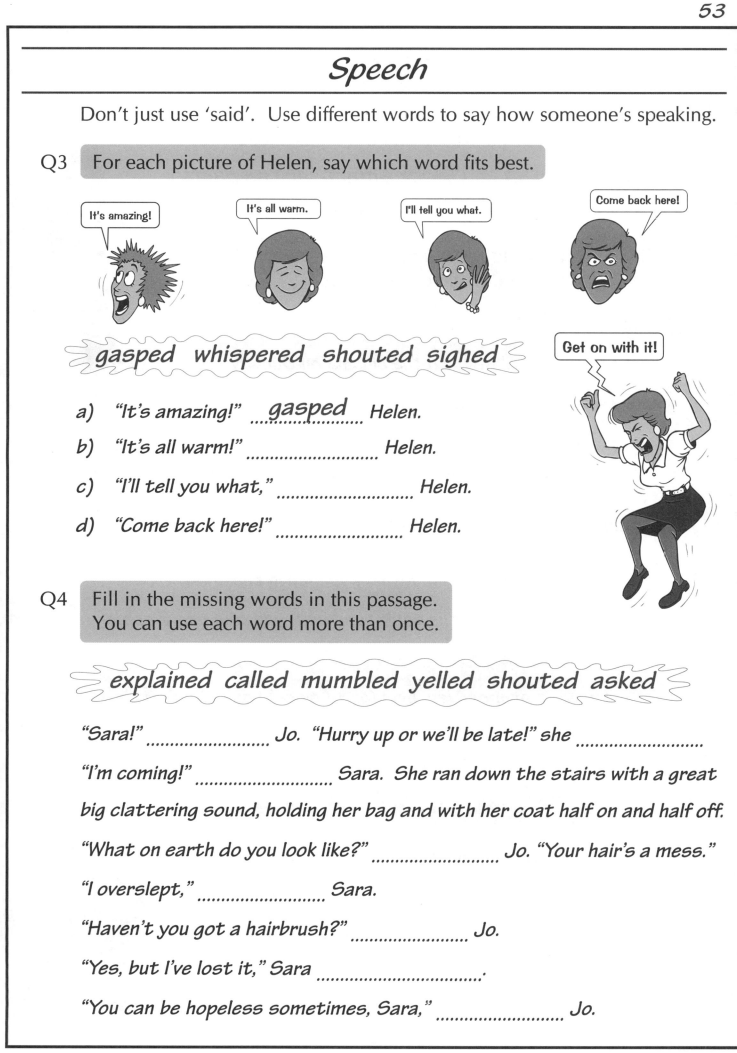

gasped   whispered   shouted   sighed

a) "It's amazing!" ....gasped........ Helen.

b) "It's all warm!" .... Helen.

c) "I'll tell you what," .... Helen.

d) "Come back here!" .... Helen.

Q4 Fill in the missing words in this passage. You can use each word more than once.

explained   called   mumbled   yelled   shouted   asked

"Sara!" .... Jo. "Hurry up or we'll be late!" she ....

"I'm coming!" .... Sara. She ran down the stairs with a great

big clattering sound, holding her bag and with her coat half on and half off.

"What on earth do you look like?" .... Jo. "Your hair's a mess."

"I overslept," .... Sara.

"Haven't you got a hairbrush?" .... Jo.

"Yes, but I've lost it," Sara ....

"You can be hopeless sometimes, Sara," .... Jo.

Joining Sentences

You can join two short sentences together to make one longer one.
There are lots of words you can use to join two sentences.

I'm dressing up so I'll look smart for the party.

'So' joins the two bits of this sentence.

Q1   Circle the words in these sentences that are
      joining parts of the sentences together.

I was thirsty (so) I drank a glass of milk.

I played tennis and went to the cinema on Sunday.

Betsy was just about to throw them away when she heard a noise.

Words like '**and**', '**if**' and '**because**' all do slightly different jobs.
If you use the wrong one, your sentence will mean something else.

Q2   Circle the best word to fill each gap.

Sometimes both will make sense.
But one will always make <u>better</u>
sense than the other.

You looked daft (then / (when)) you fell in the snow.

I left the cake on the table (so / and) you could have some.

Brian listens to the radio (while / because) he washes up.

I haven't stopped laughing (and / since) I saw Sam's haircut.

Q3   Use the words in the box to fill in the gaps in these sentences.

when if while although because

It's hot ...... *because* ...... *Sam turned the heater up.*

I'll keep the door shut .... *I'm busy with work.*

I love Chinese food .... *I don't eat it very often.*

You can come in .... *I've finished.*

I'll give you a fiver .... *I win the Lottery.*

Joining Sentences

Some words let you know **when** things happened.

These say what happened **next**.

then   **after that**

while   **meanwhile**

These say that something happened at the **same time** as something else.

Q4   Read this little story about getting up in the morning.
Then answer the two questions below.

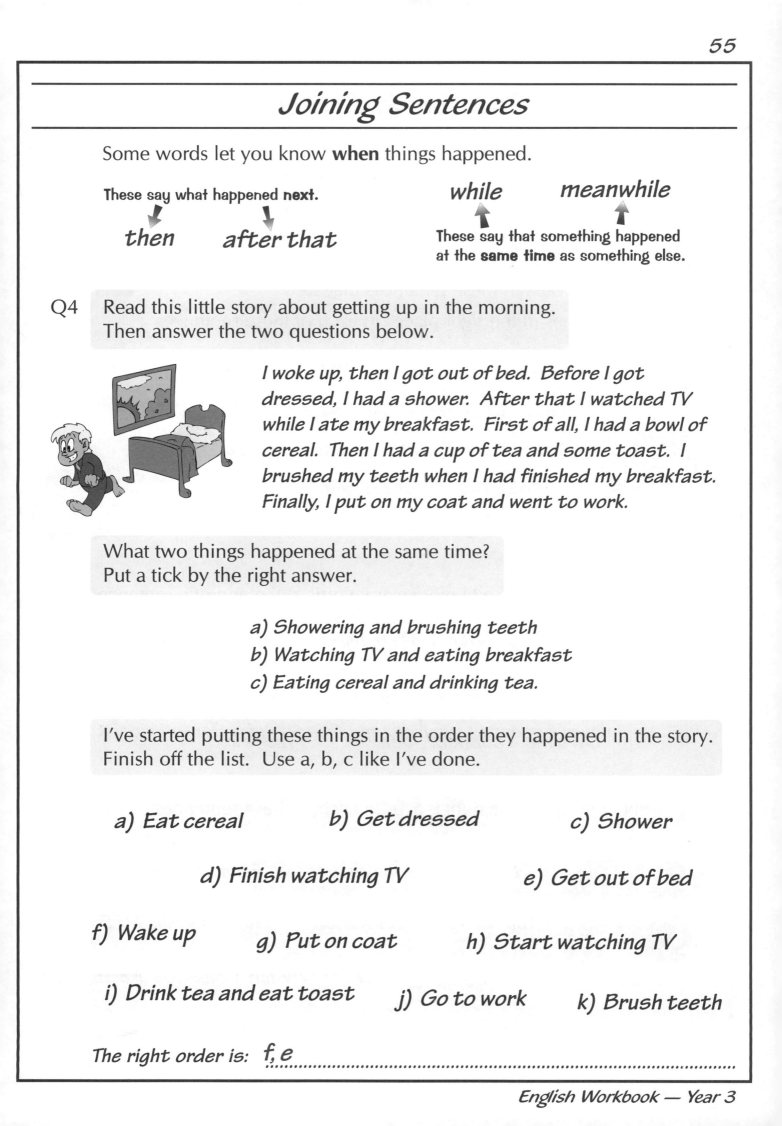

I woke up, then I got out of bed. Before I got dressed, I had a shower. After that I watched TV while I ate my breakfast. First of all, I had a bowl of cereal. Then I had a cup of tea and some toast. I brushed my teeth when I had finished my breakfast. Finally, I put on my coat and went to work.

What two things happened at the same time?
Put a tick by the right answer.

a) Showering and brushing teeth
b) Watching TV and eating breakfast
c) Eating cereal and drinking tea.

I've started putting these things in the order they happened in the story.
Finish off the list. Use a, b, c like I've done.

a) Eat cereal   *b) Get dressed*   *c) Shower*

d) Finish watching TV   *e) Get out of bed*

f) Wake up   *g) Put on coat*   *h) Start watching TV*

i) Drink tea and eat toast   *j) Go to work*   *k) Brush teeth*

The right order is: f, e ....

Commas in Sentences

Commas aren't just used in lists. They're used to make sentences clearer.
They separate any extra bits that have been added to a sentence.

Well, it had to happen.   *As a matter of fact, I'd love to.*

Always put a comma after extra words or phrases at the start of a sentence.

Q1   Put commas in the right places in each of these sentences.

"Oh, I like your costume!" "Why thank you very much."

"Tell me what are you supposed to be?"

"As a matter of fact I'm a pineapple tree."

"Well that's just brilliant."

"Actually I rather like it."

Commas are also used before extra words at the end of a sentence.

Could I have another deep-fried ice cream, please?

They're used with people's names and titles as well.

Give me a chance, John.   *Yes, sir!*

Q2   Put commas in the right places in each of these sentences.

I'd love to, Your Majesty.   Ellen can you hear me?

You need a haircut mate.   Good morning Mr Smith.

May I go please?   What would you like madam?

Hello could I speak to Sally please?   Yes I'm very pleased John.

Commas in Sentences

Commas are used with bits of extra information given in sentences.

One of the dogs, a huge Alsatian, ran up to me.

You could leave the extra bit out and the sentence would still make sense.

Q3 Add the right bit of information to each sentence so it makes sense. Don't forget to put commas in all the right places, too.

Brazil's star player

Sue and Leon   *the team captain*

a) *Jim scored an own goal.*

   Jim, the team captain, scored an own goal.

b) *I saw my friends in the pool.*

   ....

c) *Pele scored two goals.*

   ....

Commas are also used to break up longer sentences into smaller parts. They help you to pause for breath when you read the sentence out loud.

During the thunderstorm, we hid in the old barn.

Q4 Put a comma in the right place in each sentence.

I ran for the train, but I was just too late.

After the pie fight we had to clean the dining room.

The dog barked all night but no one listened.

I waited four hours until Henry finally turned up.

Homonyms

Some words have more than one meaning, but the same spelling.

The players are in good form.

This means they're playing well.

My sister is in form 3A.

This means her 'class'.

Q1 Each sentence on the right uses the same word as one on the left, but with a different meaning.
Fill in the missing words and match up the pairs of sentences.

The wheel had a broken spoke.

Do you like my check shirt?

My suitcase is very light.

Can I go to the cinema?

Could you turn on the ....?

The old man **spoke** to me.

I'd love a .... of lemonade.

I always .... my sums.

Q2 Finish these pairs of sentences with the correct word from the list.
Use the same word with both sentences in the pair.

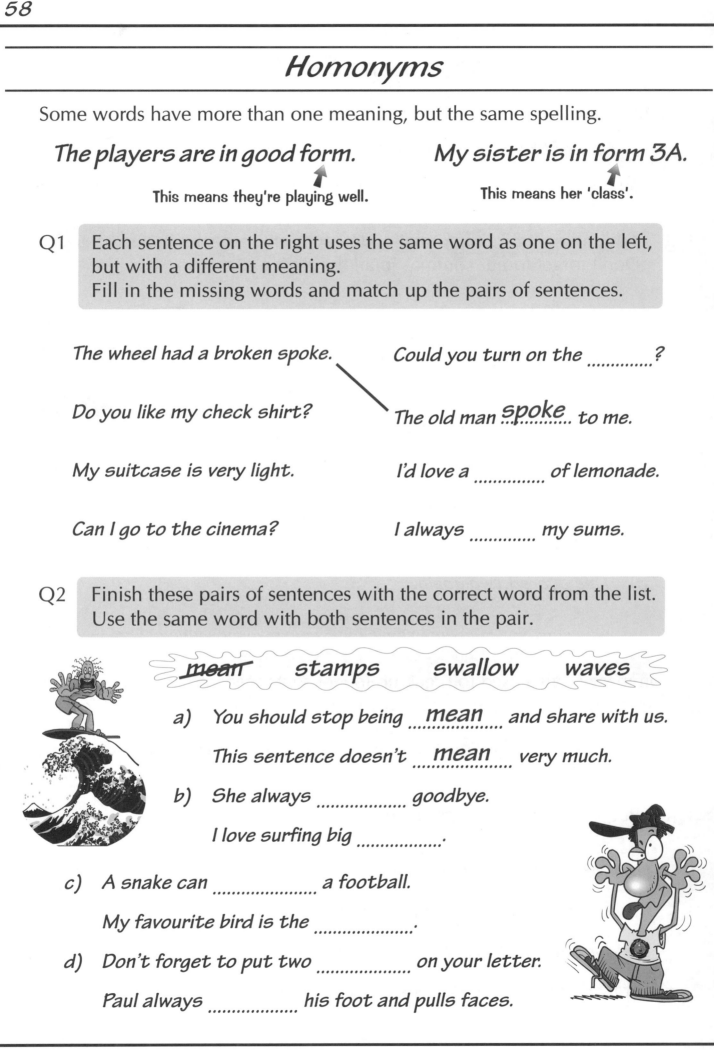

~~mean~~   stamps   swallow   waves

a) You should stop being ...**mean**... and share with us.

This sentence doesn't ...**mean**... very much.

b) She always .... goodbye.

I love surfing big ....

c) A snake can .... a football.

My favourite bird is the ....

d) Don't forget to put two .... on your letter.

Paul always .... his foot and pulls faces.

Answers

P1 PHONEMES

Q1
oh, o, oo, ow

Q2
grain — coat
her — treat
claw — foot
blue — fort
coil — bird
though — moon
push — tray
meet — boy

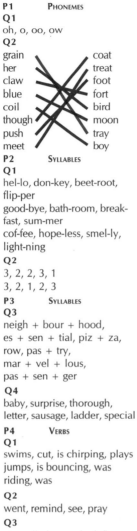

P2 SYLLABLES

Q1
hel-lo, don-key, beet-root, flip-per
good-bye, bath-room, break-fast, sum-mer
cof-fee, hope-less, smel-ly, light-ning

Q2
3, 2, 2, 3, 1
3, 2, 1, 2, 3

P3 SYLLABLES

Q3
neigh + bour + hood,
es + sen + tial, piz + za,
row, pas + try,
mar + vel + lous,
pas + sen + ger

Q4
baby, surprise, thorough, letter, sausage, ladder, special

P4 VERBS

Q1
swims, cut, is chirping, plays
jumps, is bouncing, was
riding, was

Q2
went, remind, see, pray

Q3
ate, called, squeaked, flew

P5 VERBS

Q4

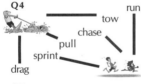

run
tow
chase
pull
sprint
drag

Q5
knocked, dived, stamped, brushed, bounced, posted, swept, groaned

P6 CAPITAL LETTERS & FULL STOPS

Q1
Mark liked the wind in his hair.
Sandra liked roast cucumber sandwiches.
"I don't like lard," said Jim. I agreed with him.
It's only eight o'clock. It's not too late.

Q2
Little Lenny just loved eating trees.
The old man had green hair.
Baby Frieda loved licking lollipops.
My neighbour trod on her marshmallows.
She bought some shoes made from kippers.

P7 QUESTIONS & EXCLAMATIONS

Q1
question, exclamation, question, question, exclamation

Q2
?, !, ?, !, ?, !, !, ?, ?, !

P8 SPELLING '-ING' WORDS

Q1
passing, doing, sleeping, feeling
going, thinking, fighting, rusting

Q2
hitting, swimming, rubbing, rapping
stopping, skipping, flapping, spitting

Q3
a) swimming, b) digging,
c) tipping, d) shopping,
e) flapping

P9 SPELLING '-ING' WORDS

Q4
making, riding, shaking, hiding, taking

Q5
tying, dying, lying

Q6
baking, carrying, slipping, falling, dancing

P10 SPEECH MARKS

Q1
a) "I've got a lovely bunch of coconuts," said Anna.
b) "You can't play football on the dinner table," said Pete.
c) "There's a hole in that bucket," said Pete.
d) "Oh dear, this doesn't look right," said Kirsty.
e) "I see no ships," said Captain Pugnose.
f) "I don't know where they are," replied Aisha.
g) "Can you mend my bike?" asked Luke.
h) Tom said, "You can't fit a pig in a paper bag!"

Q2
a) asked, b) replied, c) said.
d) asked, e) replied, f) asked
...or any suitable answers.

P11 SPEECH MARKS

Q3
a) "You haven't tidied your room," shouted Dad.
b) Bernice said, "It's no good, I'll never know my times tables."
c) Graham said, "This elephant smells a bit funny."
d) Sally whispered, "The moon reminds me of marshmallows."

Q4
asked, replied, muttered, shouted, squealed, yelled
...or any suitable answers.

P12 COMMAS IN LISTS

Q1
a) chocolate,
b) spoon, knife,
c) man, dog,
d) tea, coffee,

Q2
a) I dropped my notes, a pen, a pencil and a donkey.
b) We saw lions, elephants, giraffes, zebras and gibbons.
c) Do you want lemming squash, beetroot juice or camel soup?
d) They gave us a choice of catfish, dogfish, swordfish or goldfish.

Q3
a) There are sandwiches, crisps, cakes and biscuits.
b) We could play tennis, badminton, football or netball.
c) I want a computer game, some Lego, a fluffy toy and a bike.

P13 COMMAS IN LISTS

Q4
a) I've just eaten a plate of beans, a squashed cabbage, three bulbs of garlic and a load of fairy cakes.
b) Martians have long spiky fingers, big eyes, very curly ears, wrinkled green skin, really tall antennae and pointy teeth.

Q5
a) Xena went to the shops and bought a tube of toothpaste, a pair of football boots, a teddy bear and a broken skateboard.
b) In this room I can see a plant, a pair of scissors, a pencil and a shirt.
c) For Christmas, my mum wants a fast car, a holiday to Mars, a pair of sunglasses and a pencil.
...or any suitable answers.

P14 PREFIXES

Q1
un-, dis-, re-, pre-, de-
im-, re-, un-, de-, pre-

Q2
impossible, unpleasant, disappear, unhappy, unkind, unafraid
disagree, undress, dishonest, undo, unwrap, unmarried

P15 PREFIXES

Q3
repay, reappear, redo, relaunch

Q4
preview, prepay, to wash in advance, to cook in advance, prehistory

Q5
untie, unusual, untrue, impolite, rearrange, preheated

P16 SYNONYMS

Q1
big — little
small — tidy
happy — adore
smell — cheerful
neat — stink
love — huge

Q2
cold, wet, horrible, shake, terrible, dirty, twist

P17 SYNONYMS

Q3
The synonyms are:
sack, bag; sea, ocean;
street, road; lorry, truck;
pig, hog

Q4
nice, sweet, gentle
slim, thin
happy, glad
small, little, tiny
...or any suitable answers.

Q5
started, starving, bit, gigantic or big, stack, stuffed

P18 WORDS ENDING WITH -LE

Q1
eagle, handle, needle
marble, table, puzzle

Q2
sparkle, cradle, bottle, turtle, double, jumble, people, pebble

P19 SILENT LETTERS

Q1
e; g; w; h; h
w, e; k; k; w, e; w

Q2
k, h, g, h, w
w, e, w, h, k

P20 ADDING '-Y' TO WORDS

Q1
rocky, snowy; squeaky, fizzy

Q2
flaky, shaky; shady, nosy

Q3
muddy, runny, grubby, furry, skinny, stubby, funny

P21 ADDING '-ER' AND '-EST'

Q1
smaller, nastier, darker, funnier, warmer
lightest, lowest, coldest, warmest, driest

Q2
bigger, fatter, hotter, fitter, thinner, wetter
biggest, fattest, hottest, fittest, thinnest, wettest

P22 SINGULARS AND PLURALS

Q1
houses, lamps, cards, drums

Q2
The plurals are:
ladybirds, spots, eyes, wings, ants, legs

Q3
cinema, school, spaceship, teacher, girls, alien

P23 SINGULARS AND PLURALS

Q4
peaches, tables, cars, dresses, switches; pianos, dishes, wheels, boxes, potatoes

Q5
√ jellies, √ flies, ✗ puppys
√ valleys, √ boys,
✗ chimneies, ✗ babys
puppies, chimneys, babies

P24 COMPOUND WORDS

Q1
toothbrush, raincoat, bedroom, dishcloth

Q2
lace, cup, room, time

Q3
a) postbox, goldfish
b) hairbrush, teabag
c) grandmother, football
d) sheepdog, sunshine

P25 COMPOUND WORDS

Q4
eyebrow, eyeball, toenail
eyelash, armpit, fingernail, footprint

Q5
grandmother, raincoat, sunshine, teacup, saucepan, flowerpot, blackbird, birdcage

P26 SUFFIXES

Q1
really, careful, darkness
helpful, powerless, madly

Q2
hope, different, thought
sad, good, colour

Q3
happily, busily, prettily
scarily

P27 SUFFIXES

Q4
hunter, worker, singer, golfer, banker; teacher, helper, walker, thinker, preacher

Q5
walker, walking; painful, painless; helpful, helpless, helping; helper; colourful, colourless, colouring; friendly

P28 CONFUSING WORDS

Q1
here — their
right — write
new — wear
where — hear
there — knew

Q2
1. no, know
2. which, witch
3. would, wood

P29 CONFUSING WORDS

Q3
hole, hour, hear, sum

Q4
too, too, to, two, to, to

Q5
knows, write, know, where, would

P30 APOSTROPHES

Q1
we're, she's, I'll, you've
they're, Sue's, we'd, Jim'll

Answers

Q2
don't, you've, isn't, there's

P31 APOSTROPHES
Q3
you are, I am, is not
we have, did not, would not

Q4
who's, there's, don't, don't, he'll

Q5
Tim is, Tim has; I had, I would

P32 DEFINITIONS
Q1

present .... a ship etc

lighthouse .... a thing you use to speak etc.

telephone .... a tower etc.

submarine .... something you give etc.

Q2
The correctly defined words are:
yoghurt, exercise, point, nightmare, hand

P33 DEFINITIONS
Q3
the sea, bread, green; seventh, money, seeing

Q4
The correct definitions are:
meat from a pig;
a kind of bad, ugly fairy;
the empty space down the side of a page;
an imaginary line around the middle of the earth.

P34 ALPHABETICAL ORDER
Q1
a) cake, margarine, sausage, toffee
b) coffee, dawn, none, sleep
c) eggs, mountain, rhubarb, snake
d) banjo, drum, flute, pipe

Q2
a) can, chair, comb, crop
b) dark, decide, dog, drink
c) give, gland, goat, groan
d) pack, peace, pie, prowl
e) banner, beat, bite, bland, bowl, brown, buck
f) aardvark, aeroplane, animal, apple, astronaut, attack

P35 INTERNAL WORDS
Q1

message .... word
every .... age
sword .... should
shoulder .... lie
believe .... ever

Q2
tea, ear; shall, all, hall, allow, low; is, land; he, hear, ear; fat, her
...or any suitable answers.

Q3
sling, able, king, ear; me, antic, sing, rid

P36 ALPHABETICAL ORDER
Q1
deer, cows, moose, fish, aeroplanes, aircraft

Q2
a) mice, b) feet, c) children, d) women, e) geese, f) moose

P37 SINGULAR AND PLURAL
Q3
calves, loaves, knives
leaves, elves, scarves

Q4
beliefs, proofs, roofs, reefs

Q5
wolves, roofs, scarves, thieves, loaves

P38 OPPOSITES
Q1

buy .... full
lose .... small
big .... sell
empty .... rough
smooth .... win

Q2
hard, false, young, light, forget

Q3
a) Helen is always kind to gerbils.
b) Boris was wearing an old wig.
c) Martin's emptied his cheeks.
...or any suitable answers.

P39 OPPOSITES
Q4
a) happy, lose; I'm always sad when United win.
b) rough, sharp; The dinosaur's skin was smooth and its teeth were blunt.
c) rich, poor; Robin Hood stole from the poor to give to the rich.
...or any suitable answers.

Q5
It was dark and cold in the forest. The air was dirty and stale. All around me were big, old trees, and as I walked along the path I felt frightened. I knew I was in a dangerous place.

P40 ADJECTIVES
Q1
a) The cunning thief climbed in through the open window.
b) The spider had eight hairy legs, and wore a stripy hat and pullover.
c) The man wore a smart suit and was walking a green frog.

Q2
big, fierce, terrified, brave, worried

P41 ADJECTIVES
Q3
round, square, triangular; happy, sad, bored; yellow, orange, blue; big, large, tiny

Q4
a) new, wooden
b) smart, friendly
c) rough, scaly
d) oval, rectangular

P42 MORE PREFIXES
Q1
misread, mistake, mistreat, misjudged, misspell

Q2

coincidence .... live etc.
co-author .... work etc.
coexist .... write etc.
cooperate .... when two etc.

P43 MORE PREFIXES
Q1
exhibition, explained, extinct, exhibits, exhausted, excellent

Q2
non-, anti-, non-, non-, non-, anti-, anti-

P44 PRONOUNS
Q1
she, they, I, you, it, we, us

Q2
Kit, Kit, the hammer, the twins, the twins, the twins, the twins

P45 POSSESSIVE PRONOUNS
Q1
our, his, my, their, theirs, our, their, its

Q2
my, her, his, hers, my, theirs, our
(...or any suitable answers)

P46 VERBS & PRONOUNS
Q1

you .... she
I .... grow .... they
he .... grows .... you
we .... it

Q2
looks, find, eats, make, know, walk, rides, smell

P47 VERBS & PRONOUNS
Q3
is, are; is, are; am, is; are, am

Q4
They are famous pirates.
He is going to make us walk the plank.
We bury treasure on islands.
Then we forget where we put it.
She is my parrot. She speaks Chinese, English, and Spanish.

P48 PLURAL SENTENCES
Q1
singular, singular, singular, plural, plural

Q2
The girls can really juggle.
We are feeling very tired.
The boys couldn't believe their eyes.

P49 FIRST, SECOND & THIRD PERSON
Q1
first person, third person, third person, first person, third person

Q2
second, first, second; third, third, third

P50 COLLECTIVE NOUNS
Q1
herd, group, flock, army

Q2
shoal, bunch, litter, swarm, team, fleet

P51 CAPITAL LETTERS
Q1
a) America, Disneyland
b) My, Miguel, Spain
c) Tom's, Christmas
d) My, Kirsten, Monday, Eastenders

Q2
a) We're going to Scotland at Easter.
b) My birthday is in May.
c) My friend supports Arsenal, but I can't stand football.

Q3
Mary had a little fish,
Its fins so bright and blue.
She never went out anywhere
If the fish could not go too.

P52 SPEECH
Q1
a) "I think I'll skip lunch today," said Bob.
b) Pam said, "It looks like it's going to rain."
c) "That can't be right," said Sarah.

Q2
a) "It's a bit windy!" yelled Geoffrey.
b) "Where do you think you're going?" asked Billy's mum.
c) "Is it okay if we teach the dog how to fly?" asked Billy.

P53 SPEECH
Q3
a) gasped, b) sighed, c) whispered, d) shouted

Q4
called, shouted, yelled, asked, mumbled, asked, explained, shouted
...or any suitable answers.

P54 JOINING SENTENCES
Q1
so, and, when

Q2
when, so, while, since

Q3
because, while, although, when, if

P55 JOINING SENTENCES
Q4
b) Watching TV and eating breakfast.
f, e, c, b, h, a, i, d, k, g, j

P56 COMMAS IN SENTENCES
Q1
"Oh, I like your costume!"
"Why, thank you very much."
"As a matter of fact, I'm a pineapple tree."
"Well, that's just brilliant."
"Actually, I rather like it."

Q2
I'd love to, Your Majesty.
You need a haircut, mate.
May I go, please?
Hello, could I speak to Sally, please?
Ellen, can you hear me?
Good morning, Mr Smith.
What would you like, madam?
Yes, I'm very pleased, John.

P57 COMMAS IN SENTENCES
Q3
Jim, the team captain, scored an own goal.
I saw my friends, Sue and Leon, in the pool.
Pele, Brazil's star player, scored two goals.

Q4
I ran for the train, but I was just too late.
After the pie fight, we had to clean the dining room.
The dog barked all night, but no one listened.
I waited four hours, until Henry finally turned up.

P58 HOMONYMS
Q1
Could you turn on the light?
The old man spoke to me.
I'd love a can of lemonade.
I always check my sums.

Q2
a) You should stop being mean, and share with us.
This sentence doesn't mean very much.
b) She always waves goodbye.
I love surfing big waves.
c) A snake can swallow a football.
My favourite bird is the swallow.
d) Don't forget to put two stamps on your letter.
Paul always stamps his foot and pulls faces.

Answers are always given column by column, not row by row.